The Golden Guinea book of
Heavy Horses
Past and Present

The Golden Guinea book of Heavy Horses

Past and Present

Edward Hart

The stallion man. Hundreds of stallions walked the British countryside during spring and early summer breeding seasons in these gears, which include a 'roller' on the horse's off side to prevent him turning his head too far to the left

David & Charles
Newton Abbot   London   Vancouver
North Pomfret (Vt)

This book is dedicated to those who kept the
heavy horse flag flying, when all seemed lost.

ISBN 0 7153 7146 0
Library of Congress Catalog Card Number 75-31325

Set in Monophoto Times
and printed photolitho in Great Britain
by Ebenezer Baylis & Son Limited
The Trinity Press, Worcester, and London
for David & Charles (Publishers) Limited
Brunel House   Newton Abbot   Devon

Published in the United States of America
by David & Charles Inc
North Pomfret   Vermont 05053   USA

Published in Canada
by Douglas David & Charles Limited
1875 Welch Street   North Vancouver   BC

Contents

Foreword

When I was approached by the Shire Horse Society in 1971 to provide sponsorship for an extra day's horse ploughing at the World Ploughing Championships, held that year near Taunton in Somerset, I little thought that eventually the Shire Horse Society would do me the honour of asking me to be their President.

My company, J. R. Parkington & Co. Ltd., wine shippers, agreed to put up the prize money for two extra days of ploughing before the British National Championship and, instead of the six teams that had originally entered, twenty-three pairs ploughed for the championship. Since that day, the name of J. R. Parkington and Golden Guinea, the sparkling wine after which our sponsorships are named, has become well-known amongst those who follow the fortunes of the heavy horse.

We are justly proud that our activities have been in a small way responsible for the revival in interest in heavy horses in Britain, and we are more than pleased that we have been able to keep alive some of the traditions and pageantry of the English countryside. However, sponsorship is a two-way vehicle. We are only able to continue to support events if we receive the support of the general public.

It may be just a coincidence, but I am the first President of the Shire Horse Society since 1959 who is not a brewer. The heavy horse world in general must owe an immense debt of gratitude to those breweries who, during the dark days of the 1950s and 1960s when the heavy horse was in grave danger of extinction, upheld a demand for good geldings and enabled breeders to keep mares and stallions for commercial reasons, not just out of sentiment.

Edward Hart's book comes at an opportune time. The four breeds of heavy horse are enjoying a tremendous revival both in numbers and spectator interest. The throng of people around the show ring when the heavy horses turnout or the breed classes are in, is evidence enough of that. We hope that *The Golden Guinea Book of Heavy Horses Past and Present* will provide a useful and enjoyable source of reference to all those who feel as I do that the heavy horse is an integral part of Britain's heritage.

Ralph Gilbey

Preface

by David Kay, past-president, Shire Horse Society

It was in the late 1940s and early 50s that the heavy horse appeared to be plunging to the depths of virtual extinction. It seemed then that everything that had been written, said and done would simply find its resting place in the archives of history. However, due to changing circumstances the Shires, Suffolks, Clydesdales and Percherons are not only still with us, but in increasing numbers. Who would have thought in those days of depression that twenty-five years later a book would be published dealing not only with a brief history of the four breeds, but experience and knowledge which can be put to present day use?

Edward Hart's book is of interest to people in all walks of life, particularly brewers, farmers, industrialists, breeders and admirers of the heavy horse. It is equally applicable to heavy horse enthusiasts in other lands, particularly the United States of America and Canada where a mini revival is taking place. Full of interesting photographs, and pen and ink drawings by the Misses Alderson, this fascinating book deals with every aspect of the heavy horse including stabling, yoking and harness, carts and waggons, and the decorated horse, not forgetting the blacksmith and his forge.

I should like to quote from Chapter 5: 'At three o'clock on a mid-summer morning, with trace chains clanking and Diamond and Beauty snorting and stumbling down the steep cutting, we set off to cut grass while the rest of the world was asleep . . . ' Maybe it is now awake to the fact that the heavy horse is very much with us once again.

Introduction

In the 1960s heavy horses could hardly be given away. Today it is difficult to value a good one. This dramatic turn-round in a class of livestock not usually associated with sudden change is a cause for relief, wonder, and above all, rejoicing. The heavy horse has played as steady a part in British and American history as its own ability to lean in to a massive load. For two centuries it provided the main motive power on farms, and much in towns.

Then came the internal combustion engine and the hastening decline in heavy horse numbers, a procession accelerated by World War II. In the 1950s and '60s only a handful of breeders remained, retaining their horses from love and habit rather than through real hope. The machine had done what was deemed impossible; it accomplished even the most precise farm tasks. The heavy horse seemed to be dying on its feet. Breweries provided the sole market for quality animals, using them for delivery and advertisement. Indeed, the grooms' dedication and skill must have been one reason for the heavies' retention.

8

Then surprisingly the United States, cradle of the internal combustion engine, became interested. Exports thrived. A good heavy was at last worth money. Breeders saw a chink of light. In 1970 a party of forty American and Canadian horsemen visited the Peterborough Heavy Horse Show in Eastern England, made friends and bought horses. They came back for more.

The heavy horse was pulling out of the doldrums, but still faced difficulties common to all breeds small in numbers. There were insufficient stallions of quality because it paid to geld the best for the USA or for use in cities as draft animals. To overcome this barrier, the British Horserace Betting Levy Board and breed societies financed Stallion Premium Schemes, awarding sums to owners of the right type of stallion and ensuring a geographical spread wide enough to bring approved sires within the range of every breeder.

'Real worth in horseflesh is never put out of demand by the changes of man's habits; when it ceases to be of service in one respect it is sure to come into use in another.' Sir Walter Gilbey's words prove true as we see a resurgence of the heavy horse, based partly as an antidote to the modern industrial society. A heavy horse stable has that reassuring quality so often lacking in twentieth-century life. The clomp of hooves on the hard floor, and the rustle and smell of clover hay pulled from the rack, contrast so completely with the garage atmosphere of today.

Heavy horses are now in great demand for fêtes and carnivals, even having their own open days on farms. They attract crowds wherever they go; at ploughing matches a score of keen eyes will track the horsedrawn furrow for every pair watching the tractors. Large crowds watch multiple hitches in America, and especially the Milwaukee parade. Canada has pulling competitions and fairs, sleigh rides and draft horse queens. So popular are farms where these horses are kept that new stables are planned with viewing galleries in mind.

So the heavies are back with a bang. In this book I hope to capture something of the work and sweat, mishaps and tragedy, fun and companionship of their world. It gains strength as surely from each new enthusiast as from each new crop of foals on spring pasture.

1 The Shire

' . . . The Shire horses, ponderous living machinery, magnificent and ungainly. The hair spreading about their hoofs gives their legs a tree trunk sturdiness. The manes and tails are plaited and beribboned, and they wear halters of red or yellow leather studded with brass that flashes starrily as they toss their heads. The horses are halted, some pawing the ground, others with feet well spread, immovable as rocks.'

Adrian Bell, *Corduroy*

'Lofty, massive, shapely, with fine quality of bone, hair and hoof, free and lissome movement of muscle and limbs, noble and masculine deportment' was a former Shire Horse Society secretary's description of a breed stallion. It would serve equally well today. The Shire is a heavy animal whose natural pace is the walk, whose power is gained largely from its weight, whose temperament is essentially placid and who has the courage to pull again and again.

There is an essential rightness about a load of corn or timber drawn by a team of straining Shires. The sight of a matched team coming over the brow of a hill filled British Prime Minister Stanley Baldwin with faith and confidence, and today the call of 'Here come the Shires' sends a tingle of anticipation through crowds at London's famous Horse of the Year Show.

The minimum height for a Shire stallion is 16·2 hands, the average about 17·2 hands while mares should be at least 16 hands. The mare should be long and deep, with free action, of a feminine and matronly appearance; she should have plenty of room to carry her foal. Stallions, in contrast, should have a short, muscular back, and neck slightly arched to give the horse a commanding appearance. In both cases deep and oblique shoulders are required, wide enough to support the collar.

A stallion must have strong character, which is very different from bad temper, while a gelding should likewise be full of courage, active and a gay mover, and able to do a full day's work. Weight is 2,016–2,464 lb (18–22 cwt) though 112 lb (1 cwt) less in the gelding is permissible.

Leg sinews should be clean cut and hard, like fine cords to the touch, and clear of the cannon bone. Feet should be deep, solid and wide, with thick open walls. Years ago, wealth of hair or feather on the legs was a great Shire characteristic, but today the demand is for a cleaner-legged horse, with fine, straight, silky hair.

Preferred colours for a Shire stallion are black, brown, bay or grey. No good stallion is splashed with large white patches over the body, nor is he roan or chestnut. These last-named colours are allowed in mares, but it is the breed Society's wish that they be discouraged and, as numbers grow, perhaps the roans and chestnuts will be barred from registration. Early in the twentieth century roan, particularly blue roan, was a not uncommon colour, and over 100 years previously there had been a taste for piebalds and horses of unusual colours. Chestnut is a colour that Shire men prefer to leave to Suffolk breeders; despite its attractive shades it has now declined in the history of the breed.

'Grey is gradually disappearing among Shires, as among other breeds' said the 1907 edition of the *Standard Cyclopedia of Modern Agriculture,* quoting the first four volumes of the *Stud Book* 1800-82, when of 2,962 stallions, only ten per cent were greys. By 1914, this had dropped to under three per cent. In Canada and the USA, grey was preferred for work horses, and is given as one reason for the popularity of the Percheron there. In Britain, show ring fashions around the turn of the century were firmly against the grey, and of sixteen grandsires that head the list of winning strains, only Lincolnshire Lad II was a grey. In the 1940s there was a resurgence of greys, forty per cent of stallions being this colour, but today fashion has swung back to black with four white socks.

In 1878 Mr Frederick Street advocated the establishment of a *Stud Book* for Shire horses. The name, The English Cart-Horse Society, was adopted, to be changed to The Shire Horse Society in 1884. In 1880, members numbered 376; in 1890 they were 1,615; in 1898, 2,237; and by 1905 had risen to 3,781. In 1964 membership was down to 800, but by 1974 it had climbed to 1,200.

Even the names in those early *Stud Books* are evocative of their native countryside and its outlook. Dams picked at random are Lively, Beauty, Whitefoot, Lucy, Smiler, Lightsome, Blackbird and Honest Bloom, while the first Index contains 300 Blossoms! The stout sires whose names precede them are Farmers' Glory, Ploughboy, Thumper, Marshman, Heart of Oak, Honest Tom and Waggoner.

Stanley House Gay Noble, one of the best-known modern Shire stallions. Black with four white legs is a fashionable colour, being both flashy on display and easy to match. Black is black, but brown or bay may have a dozen gradations

The earliest Shire stallion of which any record exists is the Packington Blind Horse who came to notice in about 1755, disappearing about 1770. He is described as 16½ hands high, black, with white face and markings, broad breast, thick and upright shoulders, a low forehand and well-sprung ribs, thick fore-arms and thighs, short legs and good feet and pasterns. The Packington Blind Horse served mares for several seasons in the Midland counties of Leicestershire, Warwickshire and Derbyshire, where seven generations of his direct descendants may be traced.

The heavy black horses were, according to George Culley, almost universally bred through this area:

All mares are served, the male produce supplying the army, London, the south and south-west. The largest go to the capital for dray-horses, the next supply farmers for their waggons, ploughs, etc., and the rest mount our cavalry, or are trained for carriages, while a few of the choicest are very properly preserved for stallions.

Then the very heavy black horse declined in

Preponderance of white legs is shown on this class of Shire mares. Today's fine hair on the legs compares with the 'besom' type sought after earlier this century

popularity, and a less ponderous animal was favoured. Very strong horses were needed in the early days of coaching, due to the deplorable state of the roads, and oxen vied with horses as farm teams until well into the nineteenth century. At this time many areas of Britain had their local types of medium draft horses of varying colours and conformation, on which Shire stallions were used. The stallion travelling in a particular district left his mark, and an unrelated sire was used on his female offspring, but other than that there was no particular breeding policy for the everyday work horse.

In America the Shire's development has been dominated by the Truman family. The founder of the firm which was to import several hundred drafters every year was Mr J. H. Truman, who came, appropriately enough, from Whittlesea, Cambridgeshire, the countryside of the early black horses. Impressed by the lack of weight of Chicago horses while there buying beef on the hoof in the 1870s, Truman decided to take a shipload of Shires from his native Fens, to put some bulk and bone into the local stock. He held his first public auction of Shires in 1882. Several sons joined the business, including

Piebalds are an uncommon colour among today's heavies, but were recorded among earlier Shires. This pair is not well practised, and at a ploughing match set a rather snaky ridge

Dr H.H. Truman, later a noted authority on Percherons.

From 1900 to 1918 almost 4,000 Shires were imported to the USA, of which Truman's were responsible for one quarter. Unlike most buyers, they imported considerable numbers of mares which were sold at public auction. So local farmers established themselves as Shire breeders, aiding the breed's spread and, of course, the demand for still more stallions.

The Forshaws, of Newark, Nottinghamshire, were another family responsible for exporting many Shires. For over sixty years from 1870 they met the varying demands, finding that while American buyers sought a clean-legged, active horse, Canadians preferred the low, wide strong animal suitable for breeding half-bred mares.

Forshaw's were firmly linked to Truman's through a famous stallion, the grey, March King. Bred by Dr H.H. Truman, March King made a new hiring fee record in 1921 when let to the Newark Society–Forshaw's own district–for 2,000 guineas (about $5,000). Mr Thomas Forshaw believed the stallion to be the best in the country, topping 17·2 hands high, and of perfect proportions and move-

The brown Shire gelding St. Vincent's King William is farmer-owned, yet won his class against strong brewery competition. A four-year-old, he was broken to shafts in the previous October. Pneumatic tyres aid draught considerably

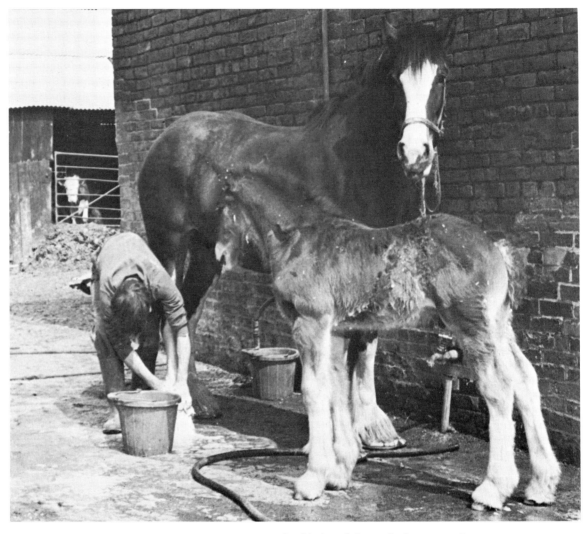

ment. He was a great-great-great-great grandson of Lincolnshire Lad II.

March King's influence reaches to the present, for prize winners at Peterborough Shire Horse Show in the early 1970s were of his line, though regrettably the grey colour has been lost on the way. The black Royston Harold, Supreme Champion in 1970, goes back to him, as does the brown Champion Gelding, Heaton Majestic. A March King son, the lively Ponton Pioneer, when having his portrait painted, danced close to have a near view of himself and put his hoof through the canvas!

This canvas now hangs in John Porter's house in Grantham. The Shire horse is more familiar with the ploughman than with the artist. As in the words of Edward Thomas:

To see him and his team all dark and large and heroic against the sky, ploughing in the winter or the summer morning, or to see him grooming the radiant horses in their dim stable on a calm, delaying evening, is to see one who is in league

with sun and wind and rain to make odours fume richly from the ancient altar, to keep the earth going in beauty and fruitfulness for still more years.

Although Shire classes have always been a feature of the major agricultural shows, until recently the number of horses forward in each class has been dwindling rapidly. Yet such is the revival of interest in Shires that they now have their own Breed Championship at the Horse of the Year Show, the 'Golden Guinea Shire Horse of the Year' sponsored by J. R. Parkington & Co. Ltd. Seven of the major shows around Britain are qualifying shows from which the Champion and Reserve go on to Wembley to compete on equal terms for the 'Golden Guinea Championship' and it is interesting that although this event is a newcomer to the show, it has already become one of the most popular spectator attractions.

A pair of grey Shires putting everything into the early furrows. Though furrows forming the ridge are lighter, the work is difficult for horses as one must walk on newly turned soil: later this horse walks in the furrow

Another fine brewery team.
Hundreds of hours of cleaning and
polishing are devoted to harness and
vehicle, quite apart from the care of
the bay geldings

2 The Clydesdale

The Suffolk Punch will keep the road;
The Percheron goes gay;
The Shire will lean against his load
All through the longest day;
But where ploughland meets the heather
And earth from sky divides,
Through the misty Northern weather,
Stepping two and two together,
All fire and feather,
Come the Clydes!

Will H. Ogilvie

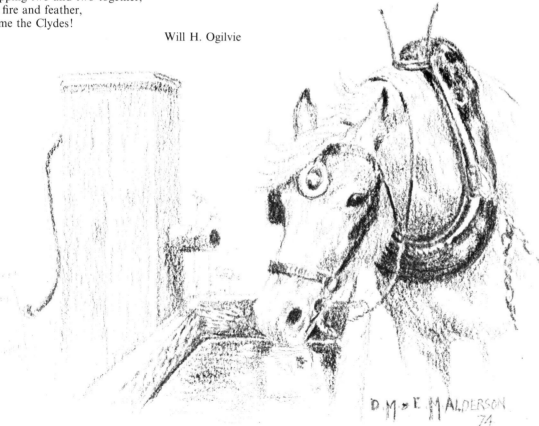

A four-day-old Clydesdale foal from County Durham, England. Work horse foals' legs always appear far too big for them. As with other young stock, a better idea of future potential may be formed at birth than after a few weeks of feeding

Scotsmen are renowned stockbreeders the world over. Their great contribution to heavy horse breeds is the Clydesdale, a fast-walking, upstanding, forceful and active horse. Black Flanders and English Shire stallions have undoubtedly played a large part in its make-up, but the fact remains that these imports stamped changes on a very sound native horse, short in the leg, active, stout and clean in the limb. Without this centuries-old foundation, there would have been no Clydesdale horse as we know it today.

The Clydesdale is called after the old name for the county of Lanarkshire, whence it originated. Tradition credits an eighteenth-century Duke of Hamilton with importing six black Flemish stallions, and John Paterson of Lochlyoch imported a Flemish entire at some time between 1715 and 1720. This latter stallion was undoubtedly one factor in the spread of the Lanarkshire horse throughout the Scottish lowlands, of which Ure wrote:

> They draw more surely, and are better for heavy work in the field, than any other. It may, without exaggeration, be asserted that no place in Europe can turn out better horses, for the draught, than Lanarkshire.

In the first and retrospective volume of the *Clydesdale Stud Book*, the Earl of Dunmore lists 1,044 horses foaled prior to 1875, and also casts serious doubts on the authenticity of the 'six black stallions' legend. He quotes Aiton of Strathaven, 1810:

> I have lived for many years . . . where these horses are said to have been kept, and made all possible inquiry into the fact, but no person in that part ever heard of such stallions. . . . I am confident that such large horses as they represented would not, when coupled with the diminutive mares in that quarter, have raised an improved, but rather an unshapely and unhealthy breed.

The colour preferred in today's Clydesdale is

"Lady Margaret"

dark brown, with a more or less defined white stripe on the face, and white socks. Light bays and roans are fairly numerous, and blacks are also found. A stallion should stand 16·3 to 17 hands high, and weigh 2,000 to 2,250 lb (18 – 20 cwt). A mare should top 16 hands high, weighing proportionately less than the stallion or gelding.

Mettlesome gait is a breed characteristic, and the steel shoes glint at an angle beyond the perpendicular when the horse lifts its feet in the walk. The Clydesdale's – or any heavy's – neck should be set well along its back. Its shoulders should have the maximum slope and its head be held high. If these three characteristics are combined, they enable the horse to 'fill its step' – reach right forward when its front foot goes out, and thus cover the maximum ground. The breed has large, flat hoofs, bred deliberately owing to their claimed superiority for town work. A wide-spreading frog, which cushions the skeleton against impact on the hard roads, lessened the chances of side bone and ring bone appearing (which Clydesdale men say is more prevalent in Shires!). This wide foot had the

By way of contrast, the mare shows a longer barrel and less upstanding neck and head. Lady Margaret is a Clydesdale from the early years of the century, and is of a firm brown colour to which the breed seeks to return after a preponderance of roan

disadvantage that the horse could walk less easily up a narrow turnip row.

Again, devotees stress that the Clydesdale should walk with its hoofprints almost in a straight line, not sprawling. Hocks should be turned in to aid this trait, and a Clyde must be judged from front and rear, not merely from the side. Correct action is vital. Look for this as the horse walks. Place yourself in the judge's position. Does the animal step out gaily and spiritedly, but with its legs well underneath its body rather than swinging sideways?

The Clydesdale of pre-war days had cleaner legs, and now the modern Shire has little if any more feather than its sister breed. This 'correct' amount of hair on a work horse's legs remains a debating point, some lifelong enthusiasts stressing that only the right sort of bone grows good hair, so that lack of hair is, and must always be, associated with weak bone structure. Answers to livestock breeding problems are not always as simple as they may first appear!

In tracing the development of any livestock breed, we must never under-estimate the effect of contemporary changes in other spheres. Small's iron swing or wheelless plough replaced the old 'twal owsen' wooden plough after its invention in 1763, and by 1791 all the forty ploughs entered at an Alloa ploughing match were of Small's design, all being pulled by two horses driven by the plough-man himself. This compares with the four men and eight to twelve oxen needed for the much heavier wooden plough.

Small's swing plough was such a breakthrough in agricultural practice that ploughing societies were formed in the surge of enthusiasm which followed its adoption. More people saw top-class animals at work turning Scottish soil and wanted to breed similar animals for their own teams. Ploughing matches became popular and the Highland and Agricultural Society of Scotland encouraged higher standards with Silver Medal awards.

In the prosperous farming years from 1837 to 1874, the Lanarkshire breed was gaining in popularity. Symon tells us:

Ploughing at Ponteland,
Northumberland, in a hundred-
miles-an-hour gale. The Clydesdale
team takes a severe buffeting

Come on, Clydesdale foal, show yourself! Let us see all those rosettes; surely the top one indicates a champion?

Clydesdales in North America. Hundreds of stallions have been imported from Scotland during the past century, and a Scottish breeder recently sought entires in Canada and USA

24

They were strong, docile, hardy and extremely active. The sight of a well-matched, well-groomed, spirited pair of Clydesdales in shining harness was most pleasing to the eye. Travelling stallions were sent from the Clyde valley to all parts of Scotland.

The Clydesdale Horse Society was formed in 1877, on the model of that great stud book, *Coates Herd Book* of the Shorthorn Society. In the 1912 Stud Book, 6,806 animals were listed, including 699 stallions. Exports were 1,348; not surprising as almost a hundred members resided abroad. In the eighty-third volume, 1970-72, stallions number 48, mares 143 and foals 371. Statistics for foals indicate that the majority of mares have been bred from, a most hopeful sign for the future. Colours show a change from former browns and blacks; blue with white markings through body; roan, face and legs white; light bay, mark on underbody white; bay roan, legs extending to knees and hocks white are all on one page.

If the early Shire stud books speak the language of Old England, the Clydesdale volumes reflect Scotland's story. Open the 1912 volume at random, and we find Mosstrooper, Mounteagle's Pride, Pride of the Lomonds, Mary of Craigshaws, Sally of Mossknowe and Kate of Tullochberg.

Scotland's breed soon spread to northern England, to the antipodes and to North America. The Clydesdale Breeders Association of the United States was formed in 1879, and an early pamphlet states:

During the settling and developing of America the horse was a very essential piece of property. Practically every family, whether living in town or country, owned and used one or more. Horses furnished the power that broke the sod of the prairies, pulled the stage coaches and canal boats, built the highways and railways, transported the freight and helped to win the wars. Great industries were built around the horse. Every community had a blacksmith shop and its harness shop. Many companies were organised to manufacture horse shoes, harness, waggons, buggies, saddles, and the innumerable farm implements to be pulled by horses.

Big teams were fashionable then, and Clydesdale six-horse teams won the Chicago blue ribbon on all but one of twenty-two times from 1913 to 1936. Yet the draft horse was falling from favour, and breeding in the eastern states, hitherto dominant, declined. Small farmer breeders of the cornbelt and western ranchers sustained it. A notable setback occurred during the Chicago Stockyard Fire, 1934, when the association's records were destroyed.

Clydesdales are still used in America today at Hardware Ranch, Logan, Utah. This Rocky Mountains ranch near the headwaters of the Blacksmith Fork River uses teams to haul bales of hay from meadow to barn, and to take hay and visitors to an elk herd by sleigh in winter. A registered Clydesdale stallion, Sultan's Pride, stands there, and home-bred youngsters may be reared as replacements for the present teams.

In Canada too the big Scots horses are remembered with affection. Lawrence Rye, a Clydesdale breeder honoured in 1967 when the country celebrated its centenary, recalled driving sleighloads of oat sheaves to the city market at Edmonton in the 1920s. While the horses were being fed before the homeward trip, Rye would visit the stable of Alex Galbraith and Son, stallion importers, so that he could keep up to date on new importations and pass a critical eye over the stallions. Natives of Scotland, Galbraiths naturally favoured Clydesdales, and their choice helped consolidate the breed's popularity in that part of the world.

In the 1880s a demand for quantity rather than quality sprung up in N. America, contrasting with exports of Clydesdales of the very highest order to Australia and New Zealand during the preceding thirty years. In 1884, 500 export certificates were issued, while in 1888 and 1889, the figures topped 1,000. By the late 1890s, horses with 'a bit of feather' were commanding a premium on the Chicago

Working Clydesdales at the Hardware Elk Ranch, Utah, USA. Mrs Mary Turnbow drives visitors and hay to the herd of over 400 wild elk, which have become accustomed to the horse team. The manes are clipped or 'hogged'. Leather traces are more commonly used in North America

market due to the presence of British buyers; Americans usually favoured clean-legged horses.

In 1907, Scotland had 155,000 agricultural horses, and 50,000 others. The type of Clydesdale bred then would find favour today, judging by photos of show winners. Secretary MacNeilage gave the ideal colour as bay or brown, with a white mark on the face, dark-coloured forelegs and white hind shanks.

The breed has been fortunate in a succession of outstanding sires. One such was Prince of Wales, foaled in 1866, an especially gay mover who lived until 1888. His owner, Lawrence Drew, a noted but controversial breeder, understood the 'nick', a stockbreeders' term denoting that the parents' best points combine to produce offspring of consistently higher class. Such a mating was Prince of Wales on the daughters of the Shire, Lincolnshire Lad II. Drew kept the Lad in Derbyshire, where he sired

sound fillies to send up to Scotland. This did not satisfy other, more nationalistic breeders and only deepened the Clydesdale/Shire controversy.

Despite their fine quality and beautiful action, the lines of animals from crosses of the Prince of Wales and another great sire, Darnley, frequently lacked cart horse character. The situation was saved by a grandson of both, Sir Everard, foaled in 1885, who stood 17·1 hands high, weighed 2,324lb (21 cwt) in ordinary mature condition, had an eight feet girth and measured twenty-six inches round the upper muscles of his forearm. Here was the massive and weighty cart horse needed. An indication of the in-breeding then current was the success he had when mated to daughters of Prince of Wales, while he achieved his greatest distinction by siring Baron's Pride out of a Darnley mare.

Baron's Pride, foaled in 1890, was champion at the Royal Highland in 1894, the only time he was

Baron's Pride, foaled in 1890, was Royal Highland Clydesdale Champion on his only appearance in 1894. He was grandsire of Dunure Footprint. The famous bay Darnley (1872–86) figures twice amongst Baron's Pride's great-grandparents.

shown. From 1896 he dominated the list of winning sires, regaining the title in 1908 when he was eighteen years old. Though his show career was short, he was there many times by proxy for, at the 1899 Royal Highland, his offspring claimed over half the prizes. In a class of twenty-five yearling fillies he had eight daughters, standing 1st, 2nd, 3rd, 4th, 5th, 7th and 8th. In the two-year-old filly class of sixteen entries, the 1st, 2nd, and 5th prizes went to daughters of Baron's Pride.

The stallion to win every possible trophy was Dunure Footprint, claimed to have sired more foals than any stallion of any breed. His service fee rose to £120 ($300) and in Volume 39 of the 1917 *Clydesdale Stud Book*, 146 of his foals are registered. Taking into account dead foals, those not registered and mares that were not fruitful, he would be serving 300 or more mares per season. At the season's height he covered a mare every two hours, night and day. Such horses gave that stamp of quality to the working horse which inspired Will Ogilvie to write:

To each the favourite of his heart,
To each his chosen breed,
In gig and saddle, plough and cart
To serve his separate need;
Blue blood for him who races,
Clean limbs for him who rides,
But for me the giant graces,
And the white and honest faces
The power upon the traces
Of the Clydes!

In the twentieth century's second decade, Dunure Footprint took over the Clydesdale leadership, winning every possible trophy. Born 1908, Footprint includes Darnley five times, Top Gallant four times and Prince of Wales twice, on both sides of the first four generations of his pedigree.

3 The Suffolk

'We return to the ring. The heavy horses are being paraded. The Suffolks come first, plump and glossy. Sometimes they break into a tense, slow trot, as though to ease an overflow of strength. Then they hardly seem to touch the ground, like fabled creatures working an aerial treadmill for the gods.'

Adrian Bell, *Corduroy*

Few breeds can claim that almost every animal in the *Stud Book* goes back in direct male line to a single stallion. The Suffolk can, and does. It is also a breed fortunate in its chroniclers, for Herman Biddell not only bred Suffolks, but wrote *The History of the Suffolk Horse* and compiled the breed's first register. Biddell traced the birth of Crisp's Horse, foaled in 1768, the property of Thomas Crisp of Ufford. In 1773 this stallion was advertised at stud as 'a five year old, to get good stock for coach or road, a fine bright chestnut, full 15½ hands, noted for getting remarkably fine colts.' Crisp's Horse became the Suffolk's fountainhead.

A century and a half later, in 1917, Herman Biddell died. Horse and man had at least one characteristic in common: they did not know when to give up. Early descendants of the Ufford horse were all great drawers of the sandbag, and similar perseverance was required by Biddell in his search to tabulate pedigrees and back-breeding of horses which were spread the length and breadth of East Anglia. This was, of course, in the days before modern transport.

The early Suffolk horse, according to Youatt, would tug at a dead pull until he dropped. Pulling contests were once as popular in East Anglia as they are in America today. The Suffolk gains part of its strength from the low position of its shoulder, and Youatt described matches between teams of 'horses, mares or geldings, without collars, to make twenty

A grand working stamp of Suffolk. This horse is wonderfully well muscled, yet carries much less fat than an animal in show condition. Such Suffolks tend to look somewhat top-heavy, whereas our model is beautifully proportioned. Note how trace chains are hooked onto the backband to prevent dangling and catching the legs

of the best and fairest pulls and carry the weight over the block with the fewest tifters'.

'Suffolk Punch' is a usual term for the breed, derived from the dictionary definition – a thick-set short man. The horse does tend to look top-heavy but this is partly illusory. Careful measurements show that the difference in bone structure between the Suffolk and other 'heavies' is more apparent than real, and a show winner at Battersea in 1862 measured in at 8 ft 2 in round the heart behind the shoulders.

In 1794 the Suffolk was described in detail by Northumberland farmer, George Culley:

It is probable their merit consists more in constitutional hardiness than true shape, being in general a very plain made horse; their colour mostly yellowish or sorrel, with a white ratch or blaze on their faces; the head large, ears wide, muzzle coarse, fore-end low, back long, but very straight, sides flat, shoulders too far forward, hind quarters middling, but rather high about the hips, legs sound and short in the pasterns, deep bellied and full in the flank; all deep-bellied horses carry their food long and consequently are enabled to stand longer and harder day's work. It is well known that the Suffolk and Norfolk farmers plough more land in a day than any other people in the island, and these are the kind of horses everywhere used in those districts.

Suffolks boast seven shades of chesnut. They have less feather than either Shire or Clydesdale, a valuable feature on heavy clays

As a true northcountryman, Culley was unlikely to extol any breed from the south or east without good reason, and the Suffolk of today is the opposite in many respects to the eighteenth-century animal with its flat sides, coarse muzzle and large head. Certainly, it is more pleasing to look upon.

Other writers also stressed the work system made possible by the breed's capacious rib cage. Fred Smith, a Suffolk Horse Society Secretary, described how the ordinary working Suffolk leaves the stables at 6.30 am, returning at 3 pm, during which time he gets neither snip nor bite, his deep-ribbed carcass being adapted to these long hours without food. This system is different from most other parts of the country, where a midday feed is given, either in stable or from nose bag.

Although the breed has a well-documented and lengthy history, some enthusiasts aver that it is unnecessary to refer to pedigrees or genealogical charts. 'Suffolks are always "Chesnuts". What other breed of horses is to be found that always breeds true to colour?' asked Fred Smith in 1926. And indeed, *Volume 1* of the *Stud Book* tells us:

There are seven shades–the dark, at times approaching a brown-black, mahogany or liver colour, the dull dark chesnut, the light mealy chesnut, the red, the golden, the lemon and the bright chesnut. The most popular, the most common, and the most standing colour is the last named. The bright chesnut is a lively shade, with a little graduation of lighter colour at the flanks and at the extremities–but not too much. It is, in most cases, attended with a star on the forehead, or thin 'reach', 'blaze', or 'shim' down the face. The flaxen mane and tail prevalent 100 years ago, and occasionally found at the present day, are usually seen on the bright chesnut.

This spelling of chesnut is found in other branches of the horse world. Opinions seem divided on its value and cause. On the attraction of the various shades of colour there can be no dispute.

Meticulous care in stud book establishment was followed in the early 1900s by a breeding scheme to encourage Suffolk breeding among the smaller class of farmers through what was then termed a hire purchase agreement. The Society provided each approved applicant with a brood mare costing not more than 60 guineas. The farmer paid a quarter of the sum at the time of purchase, and in return for the use of the mare paid interest at four per cent. All the Society's mares were entitled to free services by an approved stallion. The farmer undertook to take good care of the mare, not to work her unfairly, and to deliver the foals free of cost and unweaned. If all was in order he received £16 10s for the foal to his credit. He also received half of any sum over 20 guineas realised by the foal, so that he stood to benefit from extra care and attention he had given the chesnut offspring. If the foal was a personal favourite, he could bid on the same terms as anyone else.

A lighter shade of chesnut. This Suffolk plough team is richly decorated in traditional style; note the neck plaiting

Tandem yoking: pair of Suffolks hitched to a traditional iron-tyred cart. In practise the trace horse in front may be hitched only at the foot of a hill

The Suffolk made its mark too in those countries previously known as the Colonies. Its colour apparently helps resistance to heat, and when crossed with native mares threw acceptable light draft animals. Immediately before World War I, the Society granted 173 export certificates, and no doubt more were exported with no certificate.

A class of horse consistently in short supply today is the heavyweight hunter. A well-proven method of breeding them is to mate a Suffolk sire with a good-class thoroughbred type of mare, and to put the progeny again to a thoroughbred sire. The result combines the quality and staying power of the blood horse with the modified weight-carrying qualifications of the Suffolk.

Suffolk owners made a big effort when the Royal Show was staged at Ipswich in 1934, the highlight being a parade of 300 Suffolk horses. It has never been seen since, but in view of the buoyancy of the heavy horse world, only a pessimist would say that it will never be seen again.

These four Suffolk horses provide the ideal transport for bride, groom and attendants

4 The Percheron

'In 1820 Napoleon's two grey Arab chargers, Godolphin and Gallipoli, were to the Percheron what the Darley and Godolphin Arabians were to the racehorse–an undying influence stamping it with their type and colour and giving it the beautiful large eyes, splendid head and crest, and noble appearance.'

Lady Wentworth, *The World's Best Horse*

A district of France some sixty miles square is the fountainhead of a world-famous heavy breed. Le Perche lies seventy-five miles south-east of Paris, and proximity to the capital facilitated sales of horses for domestic transport purposes when the Percheron's original function as a war horse was diverted to peaceful channels.

Grey or black, though a few sorrels occur, the breed has clean legs free from feather, and a blue hard hoof which its breeders claim withstands the stop-go and hard roads of cities better than any other. These characteristics make the horses easily recognisable, remembering that greys tend to go white with age, and some old Percherons are very white indeed. In the early years of this century both heavy and light varieties were recognised, the

heavier type coming from the neighbourhoods of Vilvaye, Saint-Corme and Mamers. At that time colours included bays, roans and chestnuts.

Arab stallions were used to improve the Percheron about 1760. Since then both English and Danish stallions have been imported but though, throughout the whole of the nineteenth century, the breed was practically uncrossed, Arab infusions are still marked by fine temper. Colour, spirit and clean bone may be traced back to the Arabian influence, as Lady Wentworth, world authority on Arab horses wrote:

The Percheron is a grey French breed of Arabian origin introduced into England (1916). It is easily the handsomest of all heavy breeds. It

Dan and Jack, a team of Percheron geldings owned by W. M. Haven, Blackfoot, Idaho, USA. In addition to winning lightweight pulling contests, these Percherons have taken first place at middleweight events. Here they are complete with pulling gear

These Percherons deliver beer regularly in Sunderland, Co Durham. Vaux stable manager Major A. R. A. Wilson believes that the Percheron withstands the strain of town work better than any breed. Their legs are kept clean easily, and their temperament helps them to adapt to constant traffic noises

A team of black Percherons from Iowa. Blacks retain their colour better than greys, which tend to go white with age. Four-in-hand driving is gaining rapid popularity

originated as post horses and hunters descended from Arabians brought by Crusaders, and again by the Saracen invaders, and probably was part of the Norman cavalry. In 1753 the breed was crossed with Danish, Belgian and English mixtures. The grey Shire horse of the period being exactly like the Percheron, it is probable that an interchange took place. . . .The level quarters and high set tail must be insisted on as the original type, any divergence from which shows base blood, and the black colour sometimes seen is due to an inferior cross of Nivernais, and if really black (not the black that turns grey) should be taboo.

Oddly enough, though Percheron horses had been exported to the USA, Canada and Argentine before World War I, the breed became widely known to British heavy horsemen only when they themselves moved into France to fight. The British Expeditionary Force transport was then based on the horse, so thousands of pure- and half-bred Percherons were purchased from America and Canada, shipped to France, and used there by the troops. Brought up in the horse era, the soldiers soon realised the Percheron's value both in hauling guns and transport through deep mud, and trotting on hard roads. Then, as now, the breed revealed a marked ability to withstand hardship.

The British Percheron Horse Society was formed in 1918, and in the following four years, 36 stallions and 321 mares were imported and registered. Society membership grew until it reached nearly 500. Numbers declined along with other heavy horse breeds, the Percheron retaining a strong nucleus in Cambridgeshire, Norfolk, Lincolnshire and Durham. Present membership is 220, and demand is such that the Society has bought stock

Heavy horses play leading parts in carnivals and fêtes. These eight black Percherons haul a towering display mounted on an old waggon

from France to supplement home studs. There are now 40,000 Percherons in France, where 650 foals were registered in 1974.

The Canadian Percheron Association now has 350 members actively breeding or using these horses. Secretary Bruce A. Roy estimates that 1,500 pedigree stallions, mares and fillies are to be found in Canada; geldings are not registered. Grey has always been a popular colour there, partly because of the flashy appearance of a well-matched pair, partly because in former days, when horses were heavily employed in the vast cultivated fields of Western Canada, greys endured the summer heat more readily than horses of darker colours. Yet blacks have always out-numbered grey Percherons in Canada, as many breeders dislike the grey's propensity to turn white with age, a colour hard to keep clean on stabled animals.

Another reason for the breed's popularity on North American corn fields was that while burr-type weeds clung to the Shire's hairy fetlocks, the clean-legged Percheron remained free of them. These types of weed are not so widespread in Britain.

Some North Atlantic breeders operated on a vast scale. In 1909 alone, the late Mr George Lane, 'Bar U' Ranch, Montana, imported seventy-two mares and three stallions from France at an average cost there of $1,000 a head. In 1916, 117 youngsters were foaled on the 'Bar U' and 265 registered Percheron mares grazed this ranch.

Many livestock breed societies list a standard of points, but few give reasons for them. In 1936, the Canadian Percheron Association compiled a detailed study from a hundred judges, breeders, grooms and agricultural college lecturers. Opinion was unanimous on the type of horse wanted: thick-set, short-backed, deep-bodied, heavy-boned, well-muscled, good-going medium-sized horse with a nice head and plenty of quality. In 1936 Ellis McFarland wrote:

The head is one of the important things about a good Percheron. It should be medium-sized, lean, and fairly broad between the eyes, with an alert, pointed ear. A feminine head on a stallion is usually a sign of an unprepotent sire (one that does not stamp its characteristics on its offspring). A coarse head on a mare often

suggests an irregular breeder, an unsatisfactory dam, and a producer of rather plain colts. Large, prominent eyes are a most important indication. The vital strength of an animal is reflected in the eye.

Secretary Roy points out that styles and trends have undergone a change since 1936. An upstanding horse of ample stretch is now in keen demand, especially with owners of exhibition hitches. Yet although the 1970s demand a larger Percheron

The three-year-old Percheron stallion Willingham Andrew at the English Royal Show. By champion stallion Histon Limelight, he pushed his sire back to third place at the 1974 British Percheron Horse Show, Cambridge

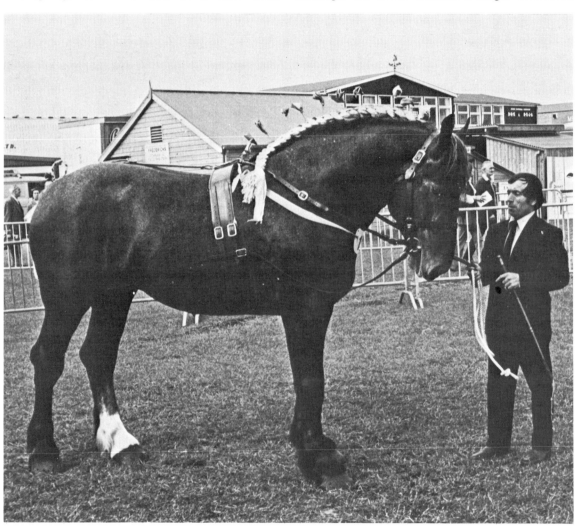

compared with the 1930s, substance, body and style must not be sacrificed, and the breed's characteristic clean-cut head and neck remain vital.

The British Percheron Horse Society similarly stresses that height is by no means everything, and that width and depth must not be sacrificed. Its height standards are not less than 16·3 hands for the stallion, and not less than 16·1 hands for the mare. From Canada, however, comes news of great demand for outstanding harness geldings of 17·2 hands and upwards. A breeder with a horse of this dimension, combined with style, quality and soundness, is assured of a spectacular market. The prices achieved for such an animal are seemingly without limit. And the best Canadian stallions have topped $4,000.

Even more surprising is the rapidly growing demand for work horses, the market for this type of stock now being unparalleled since the early 1940s when mechanisation first took full hold. Draft horses are being sought by ranchers and dairy farmers seeking economy of production. Teams are also being made up for hay rides and sleigh rides.

Recommended weight for British Percherons is 2,016–2,240 lb (18–20 cwt) for stallions and 1,792–2,016 lb (16–18 cwt) for mares. At the 1974 British Percheron Horse Show, held at Cambridge, Eastern England, the champion stallion weighed over 2,464 lb (22 cwt). Pinchbeck Union Crest, owned by veteran breeder Mr George Edward Sneath, at ten years old stood 18 hands 2½ in high. This massive black had already been breed champion five times.

Sneath has another horse, Saltmarsh Silver Crest, whose substantial claim to fame is that he is in the *Guinness Book of Records* as the heaviest horse in Great Britain, at almost 25 cwt (2,800 lb). Champion Pinchbeck Union Crest is this horse's grandson. Charlie Cook, stud groom, who took over when Fred Summerfield retired after forty-five years with Mr Sneath, is so devoted to Union Crest that he sleeps next to the box housing this famous stallion at shows. George Sneath's son, Edward, as President of the Percheron Society, presented the 1974 Championship Cup to his father, a historic event probably not repeated by any other society.

In the pure-bred mares class, at the '74 Show, T.W.J. Mott's grey French-bred Cabine won first prize, seven of the ten entries being French imports. It was apparent that the French prefer a plumper animal than British breeders, who believe that work keeps a horse fitter, and like to give their mares light work right up to foaling. Two mares in the turn-out classes were aged twenty-four and twenty-five, an indication of the Percheron's life potential.

The grey or black Percherons have won their place in the heavy horse world, a future made more secure in the UK by the Horserace Betting Levy Board's Premium Stallion Scheme. This donates £500 ($1,225), augmented by £100 ($225) from the Society, to be shared among those stallions of three years old and over which are deemed to be of sufficient merit. A wide variety of suitable sires is an essential foundation for building a breed from comparatively small numbers. This has been done once before by the Percheron, in the days of its origin. All classes of livestock show examples of dedicated breeding by a small group. The excellence of their stock combined with effective salesmanship pushes the breed far beyond its original confines, and so it is with the Percheron.

5 On the Land

How can you know?
Stomping long furrows
in the wake
of mighty horses,
to break the spine
of stubborn plough
with diamond dog-tooth drags.
Breasting the hill
with blaze of burnished brass
and proud plumes nodding.
Pivoting on headlands
their feet like iron
dinner plates,
as delicate as dancers.
How can you know
whose way has ever been
beyond the hedge?

D. B. Nixon

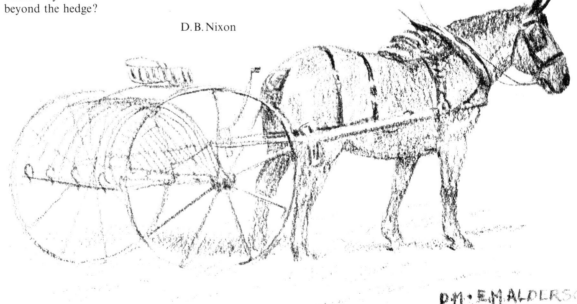

The farmer's year begins in autumn. Corn harvest is hopefully over, but sugar beet and potatoes remain in the ground, stubbles must be cultivated and ploughing started. Horses found a place on farms with large root crop acreages longer than they did on purely corn-growing farms. Autumn weather tends to be wet, and from the third week in October ground conditions usually deteriorate. This is where the horse proves its value.

Sugar beet was pulled by hand, then laid in neat rows before being topped and the beet thrown onto small heaps. The waggoner and his underlings drove down between the rows with a horse and cart each, using a blunt-tined fork called a sippet to pick up the crop. A tractor and trailer may be used but the horse and cart was simpler. When the tractor has to be moved, one man has to leave his forking, jump on the clumsy footboards, put the machine in gear and steer to the next point. With a horse, the man in charge simply called its name – 'Blossom'– clicked his tongue or said 'Get up!' If Blossom walked straight ahead, he said 'Whoa' on reaching the requisite point. If she deviated to the right he called instructions in words which varied according to regional differences, such as 'Worve' or 'Harve Back' if in Yorkshire, 'Come Here' in Lancashire or the south, with a few local exceptions like 'Cuppy Wee' in East Anglia, 'Come Hither' in Devon or 'Thow Wee' in Sussex.

If Blossom was wandering to the left, she was corrected by calls of 'Gee Back' throughout most of northern England and the Midlands, 'Gee Off' in Cornwall, 'Wheesh', 'Gee Oh' or 'Wordee' in various parts of East Anglia, and 'Wug Off' in Devon and Somerset. Scotland's terms for Left and Right were 'Hie' or 'Here' and 'Haud Off' respectively.

Potatoes were led off in the same manner as sugar beet. When the clamp was reached, horse and cart were swung round, the end door removed and the load tipped. This operation was facilitated by calling on the horse to 'Back' at the same time. In a really wet year, horses could still operate when tractors were bogged down. Horses were not displaced for such tasks until complete harvesters were designed which lifted the crop and tipped it into a container or a trailer running alongside, in one operation.

Harvest to Christmas is the busiest time of year on a mixed farm. During frosty spells, manure is led from the foldyards, usually by power fork and mechanical spreader. Horse-drawn spreaders are available, and here is one field where the auxiliary engine may yet come into its own. Horses pull the spreader and the little engine operates the spreading mechanism. Why use a rapidly depreciating £2,000 tractor to do the work of two mares breeding their own replacements? Yet we must accept that attitudes to work have changed, and that 'muck plugging' with a hand fork is no longer a popular occupation.

Cultivating stubbles follows corn harvest. The tines stir the soil and encourage weed seeds to germinate before winter, when they are killed. In the horse's heyday, cultivating called for a team of three, and modern fields enlarged for the tractor are ideal for the 'big team' of five or six to walk away with a wider implement. Horses' hoofs also cause less compaction than rubber tyres, although tractor damage to soil structure has proved less than was once feared.

Ploughing was the main job of the horseman's year. A single furrow ten inches or a foot wide and a walking speed of one-and-a-half miles an hour entailed long days to plough the requisite acre a day. 'Six till six in the field' was common before World War I, and I have heard stories of horsemen waiting with their teams on the headland until there was sufficient light. Despite this, the assertion that 'horse ploughing is work in its most pleasantly disguised form' holds true. Much of the art is in setting the plough which, once mastered, enables an experienced pair of horses to do the job themselves. In fact, one father and son, hedging at either end of a field, could turn the horses round on the headland, and set them back along the furrow of their own accord.

Holding the plough stilts or handles is easier

work than simply walking and holding the reins, as in harrowing. There is the constant tearing of coulter and breast through the soil, the creaking of harness, the white puffs from the horses' nostrils on a frosty day, the clean smell of fresh-turned earth as a new furrow is laid against the last. There is the company of horses, for the horseman like the hill shepherd with his dogs, is never lonely, though he may have no human company. I believe that a limiting factor of farm mechanisation will be the eventual unwillingness of workers to operate alone for hours on end, without human or animal companionship.

In the New Countries, very large teams of horses and mules were worked in the 1930s. In Britain they were few. The chief reason was that low wages did not encourage capital expenditure, and the farming depression was so severe that no risks could be taken. With wages at 32s weekly in the early '30s, there was little incentive to 'save a man', especially when in the closely-knit village communities of those times he might be unemployed. The patchwork fields of the arable areas had not given way to hedgeless farming, and three or four acres is not large enough for a six-horse team to operate effectively.

The first stage in ploughing is setting a rig. The ploughman sets his plough to draw a shallow furrow, and drives his team towards sighting poles. Here is Bob Powell, national champion, in action

A ridge being set by a team of
Belgians. The USA did not import
Belgians until the beginning of this
century but now its breeders claim
that it has toppled the Percheron
from the top of the USA popularity
poll with 25,000 pure-bred horses
registered, not including geldings.
The Belgian's disposition makes it
universally popular; this
ploughman, with the reins around
his shoulders, is evidently not
expecting a runaway!

To these reasons must be added the horsemen themselves. Gang ploughs with two or more furrows and six horses are fitted with seats, and seats were anathema to the old school of waggoner and foreman. 'Breeding idleness', they would say scornfully. We can well imagine the reception a gang plough would have received from those superbly-skilled horsemen of the inter-war era. They would know its arrival was watched by every neighbouring farmer and worker, and that they would be called to give an account of their stewardship in the village pub. They would anticipate the leg-pulling that awaited a one-inch deviation in the first furrow. They would consign the innovation to a gap in the hedge.

A ploughing match at Truro, Cornwall. These turn-wrest ploughs are specially valuable in small fields, as no rig need be set. The plough body and handles are swung over at the end of the furrow, and the course resumed

Today's young men are different. They have been brought up to ride, and to realise that output is vital. There is no shortage of willing horsemen, only a shortage of means to teach them. Winter jobs provided an apprenticeship in the old days, the daily routine of carting fodder to stock and manure from yards affording a time of lessened pressure compared with seedtime and harvest.

When the March winds blew and the land dried white, horses worked as long as they were able, harrowing, drilling, rolling. Corn was led out in waggons, teams were changed if there was sufficient horse power available. After the corn was drilled, root land was cross-ploughed and worked, then drilled by the steadiest horse on the place. A mistake

The press, an implement used to consolidate the furrows. Tandem yoking avoids paddling the newly turned furrows, as ploughing is carried out by other teams at the same time

Turnip drilling in the old style. A steady horse was chosen for this work. Note the taut shoulder chain and the slack breechings chain, brought into play only when backing the implement

Leading home the corn harvest in Yorkshire. The double-shaft waggon has rubber tyres, and the load was driven home with the horseman on top, using leather reins now coiled over the hames

here led to difficulties throughout the season. Old stagers were sometimes pensioned off and felt the inside of a collar only to 'drill a few turnips'.

Then came side-hoeing and scruffling, the first operation also done with a very steady horse, to shave the young plants as closely as possible and lighten the hoers' task. Scruffling with a single-row horse hoe becomes a monotonous task. On the large farms of the Yorkshire Wolds, lads would start at one side of a field of perhaps sixty acres, and by the time they had reached the far side they had to start again. They took one of their pair in the morning, and the other in the afternoon. As they said: 'No one asked if *we* wanted a rest!'

In June came haymaking. As horse mechanisation advanced this became a very busy time for farm teams. Two horses pulled the grass reaper, and if they were a smart-stepping pair, so much the better, for this highly-geared implement ran more sweetly at speed. Early morning was a good time for cutting, before the heat of the day. I well remember the sights and sounds at three o'clock on a midsummer morning when, with trace chains clanking and Diamond and Beauty snorting and stumbling down the steep cutting, we set off for 'the low country' to cut grass while the rest of the world was asleep.

As the hay dried it was turned by an assortment of horse-drawn tedders, kickers and rakes. It was then piked into small, weather-proof heaps, or swept straight to the stack by a wide sweep with a horse at either end. For speed of removal, this method has few equals, but a large force is needed at the stack side to deal with the mountains of hay. Before this machinery was invented, haytime was holiday time for horses. In the late nineteenth century, cutting on Pennine farms was by scythe, with all turning and raking done by hand. In the twentieth century it was the reverse, horses having to work hard, with little protection from flies and none from heat.

Harvest was harder still. Corn may only be cut when dry, otherwise the binder canvases become wet, shrink and tear. Thus no cutting could begin until the sun was up and the dew was off. My grandfather cut corn with four horses, changing two of them every hour, but on a small farm this was not possible. Labouring under a hot August sun, pestered continually by flies, and dragging the heavy binder whose mechanism worked via the main wheel from the traces, was no fun at all for horses. Now, of course, combine harvesters do the job in one operation, separating grain from straw and chaff as well as cutting. Yet horses were successfully used to haul combines in the 'twenties and 'thirties, one Washington farmer using a 20-foot combine drawn by 25 mules. In 1928 this outfit harvested 990 acres of wheat in $22\frac{1}{2}$ days, the team being driven by a fifteen-year-old boy.

Here is a reminder that to drive six or ten horses is

Demonstrations of horse and steam power may be seen each summer at the Ronald V. Jensen Living Historical Farm, Logan, Utah

52

not three or five times as difficult as to drive two. In many ways it is easier, for advantage is taken of the horses' well-known herding instinct, which draws them behind their leaders and encourages them to keep pace with each other. The seated operator does not have to watch his feet, which makes a considerable difference to his concentration. Steady lead horses are vital, but the rest need not be broken to the same standards, and in fact are often yoked after a few practise turns in the collar.

So ends the horses' year on the farm. The sheaves have been forked onto carts or waggons and led to the stackyard. In fine weather, harvest with horses was a pleasure. In a wet time it was purgatory, for before the days of driers each sheaf had to be thoroughly dry before stacking, or mould resulted. Fortunately, dry harvests exceeded wet ones, and the rustle of sheaves on waggon floors, the creak of harness, the warning words 'Hold Tight' as the team moved to the next stooks, the walk home with loaded draft and the ride back to the field with an empty one make pleasant memories. This was one time of year when the entire farm staff made a team, when 'drinkings' or 'bait' time was occasion for a surprising amount of farming lore interspersed with local gossip.

The combine has taken the fellowship of the fields, replacing it with a pressed switch and a solo walk home to watch television. Yet today's labour force could not possibly cope with the present corn acreage without intensive mechanisation. Sadly, for the combines dust and noise replace team spirit and horseflesh. The horseman has a double satisfaction; he has earned his own meal and he has turned out to grass the team with which he has worked all day, and watched them flick their heels into the dusk.

A knotty problem! Ploughing matches always provoke discussion

6 In War

Surely Nature was afraid
When she such a creature made;
Frightened she had wrought so well
That she did herself excel,
And her future efforts would
In comparison be rude.

H. V. Baines

Fortunately, the horse is no longer concerned in man's quarrels. 'He has fought without enmity' as Ronald Duncan says, and can now retire gracefully from the arena of modern warfare. Yet it would be idle to deny that great advances in horse breeding and horsemanship have resulted from wars or their preparation. Such advances began in England in 55 BC, as Julius Caesar tells us via Camden's translation, *Britannia*, 4th Edition:

Most of them (the Ancient Britons) use chariots in battle. They first scour up and down on every side, throwing their darts; creating disorder among the ranks by the terror of their horses and noise of their chariot wheels. They become so expert by constant practice that in declivities and precipices they can stop their horses at full speed; and, on a sudden, check and turn them. They run along the pole, stand on the yoke, and then, as quickly, run into their chariots again.

As Gilbey remarks, it is obvious from this that the horses used must have possessed strength, substance, courage and docility. The war chariot of our forefathers was not a model of elegance and lightness; it was required to manoeuvre over the roughest of ground, and the needful strength could only be obtained as the result of weight and clumsiness. Such 'carriage' horses, despite their agility, must have been open to severe punishment. Nor can we expect that the romantic figure of the knight's charger remained unscathed. Yet their wounds and even deaths must have been far less horrific than those accorded to war horses nearer our own day.

In the reign of James I (1603-25) an expedition of 10,000 men required 10,412 cart horses. They were to be hired 'in the Low Countries or where they may best be hadde' at 2s a day, or if bought outright, 'with harness and furniture' at £9 apiece. 'We think it necessary that, besides, 200 strong cart horses such as cannot be hired should be bought or continually kept for the use of the ordnance and munition.' The estimate for these Strong or Great horses was £15 a head, and county lieutenants in England were required to certify how many 'each sheire canne affourd'.

Charles I (1625-49) was also a great horseman. Not unnaturally, horses were depicted on Royal Seals, and Wyon's detailed descriptions indicate that a Great Horse was the model. In one, 'the horse's neck is protected at the back by plates'; in another, 'the King on horseback, galloping to the left, in complete armour', while Great Horses were depicted on the three seals of the Commonwealth (1649-59). Vandyke's portrait of Cromwell at this time is a magnificent representation of a heavy horse, with the long wavy tail of the period, and some feather on the legs.

In 1658 the Duke of Newcastle wrote his classic volume *The Manner of Feeding, Dressing and Training of Horses for the Great Saddle and Fitting them for the Service of the Field in the Time of War*. Amongst numerous copperplate engravings was Paul Potter's dapple-grey, a beautiful and well-shod Great Horse with plaited mane joined in a ribbon, and dated 1652. That the heavy horse was indeed recognised as the epitome of the martial charger is shown in Marshall's (1745-1819) description of the Leicester black cart horse:

The handsomest horse I have seen of this breed and perhaps the most picturable horse of this kind bred in this island, was a stallion of Mr Bakewell [a well-known livestock breeder] named K. He was, in reality, the fancied War horse of the German painters; who in the luxuriance of imagination, never perhaps excelled the natural grandeur of this horse. A man of moderate size seemed to shrink behind his fore end, which rose so perfectly upright that his ears stood (as Mr Bakewell says every horse's ought to stand) perpendicularly over his fore feet.

As was mentioned in Chapter 4, it was during World War I that British soldiers became aware of the value of the Percheron. The Suffolk was similarly praised for its ability to be on the go for

Albert Dürer's 'Great Horse', of
which Gilbey says: 'Though the
animal portrayed is not of necessity
an English bred Great Horse, it
represents the stamp of animal then
in use for similar purposes in
Germany; and from the banks of
the Elbe, stallions were imported into
England for the Royal Studs. It is
quite possible that the horse whose
portrait Dürer's brush has left us
was one of English raising'

Another Dürer engraving, 'Knight, Death and the Devil'. The Knight in this 1513 masterpiece evidently carries a considerable weight in armour, though his horse has none. The muscular neck and wavy tail are typical of the sixteenth-century Great Horse. Only stallions were used to carry knights into battle

long periods without food. 'Before I went to France I was always told to think of nothing else about a horse but legs and feet' wrote a World War I driver, and it was only when he had to look after the animals in difficult conditions that he appreciated a good converter with ample room for digestion and a hardy constitution.

Horses in war conditions obviously suffered greatly, especially in battle. In *All Quiet on the Western Front,* a German soldier describes the cries of one wounded and dying animal as 'the moaning of the world, it is the martyred creation, wild with anguish, filled with terror and groaning'. Now,

thankfully, such horrors are over and the heavy horse can settle down to playing its role in the English scene painted here by Edward Thomas:

The church and yew
And farmhouse slept in a Sunday silentness.
White pigeons nestled. There was no sound
  but one.
Three cart-horses were looking over a gate
Drowsily through their forelocks, swishing
  their tails
Against a fly, a solitary fly.

7 At Work and Play

I have always considered that the substitution of the internal-combustion engine for the horse marked a very gloomy passage in the progress of mankind.

Winston S. Churchill

D.M. & E.H. ALDERSON
74

One farmer whose horses are never out of practice has turned his teams to a double role. Geoffrey Morton of Holme-upon-Spalding Moor, East Yorkshire, has continued to work his 130 acres of level loam with horses, which has aroused much recent interest. He first turned public curiosity to good account by staging Spring and Harvest Open Days when, for a small entrance fee, visitors wandered at will, watching the teams at work. Some 2,000 people attended the first event, and encouraged by this success Mr Morton has introduced other aspects of the horse era. Blacksmith and saddler pursue their crafts, a steam engine drives the threshing machine, old tools and implements are on display, and a demonstration of 'corn dolly' making always attracts a full barn. This art of building with straw is so cheap, simple, and the end result so fascinating, that it is now in no danger of dying out.

At the Spring event, teams are seen ploughing, harrowing, drilling and rolling. The 'big team' of six or eight horses is a magnet to photographers, though it cannot be used all the time or insufficient horses are left for the other tasks. In autumn, corn is led home with horses and waggon, ploughing begins on the cleared stubble, and the big team draws harrows or discs. Geoffrey Morton finds he needs more and more horses to keep the various demonstrations in action throughout the afternoons, and for other demands on his horses' time.

More and more firms are using heavy horses for advertising. When a new shop or business is opened, the best way to let the public know is by horse-drawn waggon parading the streets. Morton's Hasholme Carr teams are becoming quite accustomed to crowds, a marked contrast to the quiet acres where they usually work.

Other companies are interested in sponsoring events at which heavy horses appear. Foremost among these firms is J. R. Parkington & Co. Ltd., an old established firm of wine shippers whose Chairman, Mr Ralph Gilbey, the current President of the Shire Horse Society, is a descendant of that famed horseman Sir Walter Gilbey. Apart from sponsoring the 'Golden Guinea Shire Horse of the Year',

Parkingtons have given sums of money to both the Suffolk and Percheron Horse Societies to encourage these numerically smaller breeds. Farm and trade turnout classes at many agricultural shows also receive Golden Guinea sponsorships and trophies as well as the major Horse Ploughing events including the British National Championship which now attracts over thirty pairs of horses as opposed to only half a dozen or so four years ago.

The heavy horse has never fallen from favour as motive power for brewery vehicles. The horse-drawn dray was at one time almost the sole outlet for classy Shire geldings, and the stalwarts who kept the flag flying have been rewarded by return of others to the ranks. Mild and Bitter, Samuel Smith's grey Shire geldings, prove great favourites among school children, as shown by the poems and letters of appreciation which follow a visit by these grey giants of 17·2 and 17·3 hands high. Grey Shires are scarce, and a potential future market here is but one good reason for continuing to breed them.

In addition to its work on the farm, the modern heavy horse is a forest animal. Various mechanical contrivances are invented from time to time to clear felled timber from woodland, but the horse beats them all on two counts: it conquers unbelievably bad terrain and its hoofs do less damage than wheels.

Contractors employed by the Forestry Commission use horse gangs much as they did twenty-five or fifty years ago. The timber may be small trees or thinnings, in which case a number of poles are chained together, or longer single trunks. In either event the horse is equipped with bridle, collar and traces, and a 'stretcher' to keep the traces apart behind the animal's hind legs. Two more trace chains lead from the stretcher to join the snigging chain wrapped round the log. On word of command the horse leans into the collar and slowly moves the log. It is steered past saplings whose life might be cut off by a crawler tractor or winch.

Specially designed wheels or tracks have improved forest transport, but many a tractor has been stranded on an unseen tree stump as its wheels

Plough setting on a foggy day.
Correct alignment is vital

claw away at leaf mould on either side and lower it ever more securely on to the obstruction. The horse cannot be bogged down in this way. If it cannot move the trunk from one angle, it tries from another. A single horse working steadily throughout a normal working day brings a surprisingly large pile of timber to the roadside, ready for the big transporters.

One horse logging team in the Rockies today consists of eight draft horses; three Belgians, two Percherons and three Belgian/Percherons, with a crew of sawyers and horsemen making this an independent unit. The team removes 'stud' trees, just large enough to make a 4 × 2in board, which

would be wasted were it not for the horse gang. To use a $100,000 D-6 caterpillar tractor and mechanical skidding equipment for such timber is quite uneconomic, as it hauls only big stuff and the rest is left unthinned. The *Draft Horse Journal* says:

But while the big 'cats' can't do it, draft horses can. A good horse and skidder can skid 5,000 board ft of stud logs daily under favourable conditions, and 2,000 ft under unfavourable ones. A team of horses can move between 8,000 and 9,000 board ft. Skidders after three months' experience can make $45 to $55 on a good day, a nice living if you like outdoor work, trees and

Scotland's famous product, whisky, under city lights. Besides saving on licenses, petrol, oil and spare parts, the horse-drawn dray is an outstandingly successful form of advertising

In the forest. The heavy 'snigging chain' is looped from the hames of the right-hand horse. During work it is slipped round the timber and then onto the horse's traces

The old mining days. This photo taken about 1912 shows a multi-hitch of fourteen horses in Park City, Utah. Teams of twenty or more drafters were needed to haul some of the heavy mining equipment. Here, a horseman rides two pairs behind the leaders

horses. A logging draft horse needs to weigh at least 1,800 lb to pull easily for eight hours a day. It can learn to skid logs in three months, and becomes a prime worker in another 15 to 20 months. It is a treat to watch a well-trained horse and skilled skidder work the 24 to 30 ft logs around stumps and trees.

These horses are wonderfully agile on the steepest slopes. They have their own code of commands. A 'lil bit' means just that, and the horse edges forward until the long log is clear of the other trees. Then it sets off down the skid trail unattended. The Merle Brown team thinned a large area in Montana, leaving 14 ft spacings between large trees, and still managing to avoid damage to young trees in

between. This could not have been done by machinery without scarring the area. Professionals say that not only does this method of extraction keep forest environment damage to a minimum, but it could well lead to more employment in the timber industry.

An American logging horse costs $600 to $800 (£267 to £356), its harness from $150 to $175 (£67 to £78) new. A three-year-old can start working in the woods but is not fit for regular work until a year later. Retirement is at about sixteen. As has been found on the canals, a horse in regular if very hard work is less liable to breakdown than one living an easier life and working intermittently.

The heavy horse is used mainly for pleasure on canals now. A barge horse must not be too tall, otherwise he cannot pass under arches or bridges. He must be trained to the job. Once a barge is under way, a very large tonnage may be moved by a single animal. Rope traces are used, joined to a single tow line fixed to a low mast about a quarter of the barge's length from the bows.

Caravanning is another work-turned-leisure role for the heavy horse, especially so in Ireland, where traffic-free roads and gentle gradients present few problems for the tyro driver. This is an ideal way for novices to learn to drive as the horses used are steady as a rock. Beginners learn a great deal about equine performance and management, mainly from the horse itself!

Few associate the heavy horse with viticulture, but Percheron Horse Society Secretary A.E. Vyse receives regular requests for Percherons to work newly planted vineyards in the South. Like other heavy horse breed Society Secretaries, he simply cannot cope with demand.

Pulling competitions have never gained the popularity in Britain that they enjoy in North America, where Canadian and American enthusiasts have drawn up strict codes of rules designed to prevent either injury or abuse, even adding 'Foul language will not be tolerated and may lead to disqualification'. Such competitions vary in detail over the continent's vast distances, but usually a pair of horses is hitched to a loaded stoneboat, or to a dynamometer which registers the pressure exerted. In some competitions, horses pull over a given distance, and at others for a certain length of time.

Amazingly, such strainings do not result in ruptures or bruised shoulders. According to Nelson Brinkerhof of Hudson, Michigan, 'The driver is not even allowed to switch his team with the reins'. And Arlin Wareing, Blackfoot, Idaho, claims of pulling competitions that, 'the horses enjoy them. They are not hurt because they are trained up to them. It is the same as with the athlete; an unfit man would damage himself attempting things that are routine to a person in training.'

The dividing line between lightweight and heavy-

For a quiet 'away from it all' holiday, horse-drawn caravans have great appeal. A proven old-stager between the shafts is the best possible teacher of horsemanship

A two-horse open sleigh. In spring the double runners are changed for pneumatic tyres. The scene is Hardware Ranch, Utah. The Clydesdales are frequently called on to haul out bogged vehicles for campers and fishermen

weight teams is usually 3,200 lb (29 cwt). A matched pair of full-brother sorrels, Cap and Barney, weighed 2,995 lb (26½ cwt) and pulled 3,300 lb (29½ cwt) over 25ft 8in at Corrunna. A Michegan team weighing 3,190 lb (28½ cwt) pulled 3,300 lb (29½ cwt) a distance of 27ft 4in.

The Waterloo Pulling Association uses a 15ft stoneboat pull. The stoneboat is a low, sledge-like vehicle piled with heavy blocks. Special harness is fitted, and in some cases a two-wheeled cart is used instead of hitching directly to the skid. There is a time limit of three minutes for each hitch. All horses are weighed in the presence of the contest superintendent, and no teamster may be changed after pulling the first load except in emergency. Other Waterloo rules prohibit drinking intoxicating

Originating in the valley of the Meuse, the Belgian is still used for dragging heavy trawl for shrimp fishing in its native country. This powerful horse is the most compact of all the heavies and was imported into North America for breeding with the rangy types used there already. In the USA they are now used chiefly in pulling competitions for which their low-set shoulders give them an advantage. Weights on the 'stone boat' can be clearly seen here and sometimes a dynamometer is used

beverages in or around the ring, and any participant under the influence of liquor is disqualified!

Three men are usually needed to hitch a team to the stoneboat in a contest. The horses are prancing and eager to pull, being off the moment the tugs are hitched, in the manner of a trap horse where all passengers had to jump in together or risk being left behind. Good horsemanship includes well-broken teams driven into hitching position at the start, and pulling together at the command of the driver.

A recent Nebraska contest attracted seventeen teams from three states. In Kentucky, the Blue Grass Horse Pullers Association limits lightweights to 2,800 lb (25 cwt), with heavyweights above 3,200 lb (28½ cwt). It conducts three state championship pulls, plus over twenty other pulls.

The crowd at Milwaukee, Wisconsin, is evidently enthralled with Richard Sparrow's ten Belgians in the Circus Parade

Wisconsin puller John Osborne has entered contests since he was sixteen. He takes his team to a horse-pull most weekends between April and October, entering against 100 members of the state association. Another Wisconsin puller, Floyd Perkins, keeps his horses fit in winter by hauling logs from the woods.

Bud Ward began pulling at fourteen, and has driven 500 miles for a single pull. Bud does his own shoeing, and earned extra money at contests by shoeing on the spot, perhaps saving the owner the disappointment of a long journey without a pull, when a shoe was thrown.

The show ring has always been an advertising medium for any class of stock, providing a goal and an outlet for the breeder with only one or two

Displays of old horse equipment are a tremendous draw. The grey Percherons haul a fire engine springing which makes a more comfortable ride than on many a carriage!

mares. The show animal and the draft animal are some distance apart; the former lives on a higher nutritional plane and is subject to less risk, and it would be worthwhile in Britain today to have competitions involving more than trotting round a level ring pulling an empty dray.

Here is Adrian Bell's description of the show ring from *Corduroy*:

> Now a prize-winner passes, a rosette upon his temple, and a rumble of applause goes round the ring. Now come mares with foals whinnying and prancing at their sides, now yearlings in the gawkiness of youth, but giving promise of future greatness. At length the whole ring is full. With deeply arched necks and shining flanks and ebony hoofs, they are like some old peace-offering between kings.

> Where horses live at the show, to stroll round their rows of loose boxes after the crowds have departed is a great experience. Owners and grooms relax after the day's excitement, heads are poked over half-doors, hooves stamp spasmodically in the cool evening air. A bunch of men discusses the awards to date. They talk of horses they have known; a Percheron that dragged its groom round the ring, a serious accident being averted only by the other grooms and the characteristic steadiness of the horses. There are scathing comments on recent imports, for horsemen always were and always will be an extremely conservative race. Owners and breeders of the past come to life, difficult foalings are recalled, the question of colour inheritance argued hotly.

> Pass into the next aisle, and more owners' names are printed on neat cards, more noses nuzzle our hands, or ears are laid back. A complete stranger walks up, and before long we are chatting about heavy horses like old friends. Heaven (as the Bishop said of the strawberry) might doubtless devise a better way of concluding a show, but to walk the heavy horse lines on a summer evening should suffice for most of us.

Spirited action from this team of Belgians from Greencastle, Indiana. Their flaxen manes are a specially attractive breed feature

8 In the Stable

The auld farmer's new-year morning salutation to his auld mare, Maggie

On giving her the accustomed ripp of corn to hansel in (greet) the New Year

A Guid New-Year I wish thee, Maggie!
Hae, there's a ripp to thy auld baggie: *(belly)*
Tho' thou's howe-backit, now, and knaggie,   *(hollow-*
I've seen the day,   *backed,*
Thou could hae gaen like onie staggie   *bony)*
Out-owre the lay.

Tho' now thou's dowie, stiff, an' crazy,   *(drooping)*
An' thy auld hide as white's a daisie,
I've seen thee dappl't, sleek and glaizie,   *(glossy)*
A bonie gray:
He should been tight that daur't to raize thee   *(alert)*
Ance in a day.

Robert Burns

'Silence is golden' has no part in stable management. Nor have Wellington boots. Creeping about in them is likely to induce nervousness in a temperamental horse, and if it does put its foot on yours, protection is virtually nil. There are good reasons for a little clatter and spirits. When your boots ring out on the stone or brick floor, and you whistle a merry tune when opening the corn bin lid, the horses know where you are and what you are about.

Greet your charges on entering the stable. It matters not whether you say 'Good morning horses' or call them by name, but say something. As you walk up to an individual animal, do so from the near side (the horse's left) and speak in the horseman's fashion: 'Come over, Beauty', or simply 'Bonnie'. The horse then knows that it is being approached and will not lash out in startled fashion.

Behind each horse are kept its gears, the general term for harness which includes bridle, saddle, trace chains, back bands and reins. Each set fits one horse and possibly no other.

The collar is common to all types of horse work. Through its shoulders the horse leans into the collar and transmits its strength to whatever is being pulled. It is vital therefore that the collar must fit correctly, otherwise restricted windpipe and sore shoulders result.

In the stable the collar is *always* hung upside down. Hung thus, it fits over a wide peg without becoming misshapen and is in the correct position for putting on the animal's neck. The horseman sets his hands on either side of the collar on the wall, lifts it, and carries it in the upright position along the horse's near side, speaking as he does so to give warning of his approach. After untying the halter shank, he places the collar over the horse's nose, pushing it up over the ears to the top of the neck.

The collar is now behind the poll, still in the upside-down position. It is swung round, always in the direction of the mane, and lowered onto the horse's shoulders. In some stables the hames are taken off completely at loosing-out time, in which case they must be strapped in position. In others, the strap is merely slackened to allow the collar to be taken off, and must now be tightened. Horsemen on the Yorkshire Wolds around the time of World War I used to say that, if they had the collar upside down on the horse when the breakfast call went, they would be too late for the meal by the time they had swung it round!

Next comes either saddle or traces, according to the task in hand. The saddle is used for all jobs with shafts, the traces for other work. The saddle belly-band is usually fastened, then checked again after yoking.

Lastly the bridle is put on. The halter must always be free or the horses may jerk their heads and break something. Most work horse bridles are fitted with blinkers, the idea being to prevent the horse being frightened by what comes behind him. That blinkers are by no means necessary is borne out by the increasing use of open bridles, one of the latest being used on Samuel Smith's two grey Shire geldings, Mild and Bitter, who face York's narrow streets and crowded traffic without blinkers.

The hame rein is hung in position, and a check made that everything else is in place; reins or strings threaded through the hame ring and over the hame; bait bags for horse and man if taken, and a coat against the rain. Then the horse is backed out, taking care not to catch the breechings on stall post or doorway. Breechings are an important part of the shaft gear. Attached to the saddle, they enable a horse to back a load or hold it when going downhill, and finally to stop it. Made of thick, heavy leather, a set of saddle and breechings is a not inconsiderable burden for any man.

Styles of harness vary from district to district. 'There is a key to every horse's mouth, if you can find it' say makers of riding bridles, but heavy horses seldom need the vast choice of bits available for riding animals. Simple iron or steel bits which work on the corners of the mouth are most common. They rest on the bars or gums of the mouth, above the teeth and over the tongue. Twisted and jointed bits are for hard-mouthed horses which are less responsive to the reins through carelessness at breaking-in. If the bit fits properly, it

Trace harness with happy rider holding the hames. These are clamped onto the collar by a top strap. The short hame rein, which restricts head movement and helps the horse if it stumbles, may be seen above the rope rein

'Loosing-out time.' The cart stands on 'stilts' as belly band, backband, breechings and shoulder chains are unhitched. The horse is then led forward, with an eagle eye to keep harness clear of hooks. After bait the horse is backed in again

Thwaites' team of black Shire geldings is one of several brewery teams which bring action and colour to summer shows. The method of yoking differs from American styles in being hitched direct to the vehicle rather than through an intermediate bar

causes no discomfort. Bit and bridle should be removed while feeding in the field, first unbuckling the throat strap.

Harness has changed comparatively little in the past half-century but in the heavy horse's hey-day it was in a state of constant flux. There was a steady flow of new patents and ideas. Harness making was a highly competitive and none-too-profitable occupation. Horsemen generally dislike innovations, so collars today are faced with leather and stuffed with straw, just as they were a century ago. Saddles are similarly padded, the groove on top being essential to take the backband chain. Substitutes for leather are most commonly found in backbands whose simple function is to prevent the trace chains from sawing up and down on the flanks.

A saddler and harness maker was once found in

The smith's craft remains as vital as ever. Schemes to maintain interest in the profession merit support

every market town, and in many villages, as was the blacksmith. Heavy horse shoes may be specially fitted with toe-pieces to assist the animal on slippery surfaces. Town horses in particular must have very careful attention paid to their feet. Plain shoes provided for the reception of frost nails in winter months are the best compromise.

Something disappeared from village life when the smithies began to close. We shall probably never see their resurgence on anything like the same scale, but the travelling farrier's life has much to commend it. No two horses' feet are alike, and the smith plays his full part in ensuring that a Shire or Percheron employs its maximum strength at a brisk pace. A move to ensure a continuing supply of smiths deserves the support of horsemen everywhere.

The smith's craft remains as vital as ever. Schemes to maintain interest in the profession merit support

Shoes must be fitted correctly for both competitions and routine work. Not all horses stand as quietly as this heavy

9 Yoking

Beside the dusty road he steps at ease;
His great head bending to the stallion-bar,
Now lifted, now flung downward to his knees,
Tossing the forelock from his forehead star;
Champing the while upon his heavy bit in pride
And flecking foam upon his flank and side.

Save for his roller striped in white and blue
He bears no harness on his mighty back;
For all the splendour of his bone and thew
He travels burdenless along the track,
Yet he shall give a hundred hefty sons
The strength to carry what his kingship shuns.

                    Will H. Ogilvie

Tight chains indicate that a sizeable
log is being hauled. The Clydesdale
mare is Blossom, the fifteen-year-old
driver is Jane Stockhill

In its simplest form harnessing consists of attaching
the horse's collar to an implement drawn along the
ground, such as a horse hoe. One end of each trace
chain is hung onto the hame hook, and the other
end onto the swingletree or whippletree. These are
made of wood, usually oak or ash, but iron is also
used. Though iron swingletrees do not break easily,
they can damage a kicking horse who, if he splinters
a wooden bar, does no damage to himself. Some of
those sedate horses on the Bayeux Tapestry were
yoked to swingletrees.

If the load is too much for a shaft horse in cart or
waggon, a trace horse is attached, sometimes only at
the foot of an incline. Instead of the swingletree, the
centre of which is hooked to the implement in a one-
horse draught, a stretcher is used. This is a strong

but light rod of wood, with a few links either side to
take the trace horse's chains, and traces which hang
in special eyes on the underside of the shafts. Trace
horses must be watched. Some have a knack of
keeping the chains tight and giving a semblance of
pulling while the shaft horse is doing all the work!

When two horses are yoked side by side, a
cobbletree, maisletree or baulk is generally needed,
unless the implement or waggon takes the swingletrees direct. The cobbletree's purpose is to equalise
the draft, so that its swingletrees are always
attached to it at either end, but it has an adjustable
crab hook in case one horse is assisted by a trace
horse. This method of yoking is called bodkin
fashion; to equalise the draught the crab hook is
placed one third of the way along, instead of in the

centre as when only two horses are yoked.

In the single-furrow, two-horse plough, one horse walks in the furrow—the furrow horse—and the other on the unploughed part—the land horse. Generally, each keeps to its own job, though some horses will take either role. A furrow horse does not require many brains; all it need do is to set one foot in front of the others at its best pace, and follow the track so conveniently marked. More is required of a land horse which must keep a sensible distance from its partner, neither tugging wide nor boring.

In-line yoking was more common in the south of England. Three or even four horses walked one in front of the other in the furrow, obviating paddling the unploughed land in wet conditions. The *Standard Cyclopedia of Modern Agriculture* calls this the

most wasteful method of yoking, but not uncommon on heavy land. The rear horse is known as the phill horse, the second the body horse, the next as the middle, and the front the fore horse or leader.

Three-horse yoking uses an adaptation of the swingletrees and cobbletree used for a pair. The crab hook is attached to the implement one third of the way along the cobbletree or evener, and an extra cobbletree is used. The principle was extended when yoking four horses in Britain, but four abreast make a clumsy team. Horses bunch and roll onto each other; they have no freedom of movement or circulating cool air. With so many skilled horsemen available cheaply, there was no pressure in Britain's inter-war period to devise newer methods, and four-horse yokes were rare.

Not so in America, South Africa and Australia. Yoking the big team became an exact science, studied by the universities as was locomotive traction. If the horse is again to be an effective force on the land, it will undoubtedly be through the big team. The main factors to bear in mind are elimination of side draught, equalising the load so that no horse can idle, and giving each animal as much room and comfort as possible.

Such knowledge was common in North America in the early years of this century, but not until the 1970s was the American method of yoking four horses in two pairs tandem used in Britain. A plough which takes 1,000 lb tractive pull with four abreast takes only 800 lb using the tandem pairs yoke, because it is possible to yoke to the true centre of draft, causing 15–25 per cent reduction. Side draft could be eliminated with the four-abreast hitch only if one horse walked on the ploughed land, which is bad for horse and soil. For tandem yoking, the front pair is hitched to the swingletree of one of the rear horses, the evener being adjusted accordingly.

The two-and-two method is the basis of all big team yoking. If this is remembered, the methods of yoking ten and twelve horses are not nearly so complicated as they appear at first. An eighteen-horse hitch of three sixes is a perfectly practical proposition.

When they developed the big team, the standard among the best farmers of the American West was to use enough horses on each implement to cover 20 miles' productive work in a 10 hour day. Teams have walked an average of $2\frac{3}{4}$ miles an hour when ploughing or disc harrowing.

Reserve power is another tremendous feature of horse teams. Horse and mule pulling tests conducted with dynamometers have proved conclusively that horses and mules have the greatest reserve power of any known power units. World pulling champions have developed 30 hp, so a ten-horse team of average horses could quite easily develop 100 hp for short periods when a burst of energy is required. Then, unlike the internal

The big team in Britain, with American-style hitch. A long chain attaches the lead horses' evener to the harrows yoked behind the hitch cart with seat attached

Belgian stallions average slightly over 16·1 hands and the mares about 16 hands high, according to the US Department of Agriculture. The Belgian ranks with the Shire, the heaviest of the heavies, weighing a ton or more, and its legs are comparatively free of feather. The nearside lead horse of these sorrel Belgians is in high condition and sleeker than one would expect in an everyday working horse

combustion engine, they are able to restore their energy when pulling well below their maximum on easier going.

A hitch cart used to be provided for the driver of a normally wheelless implement, such as harrows, but a good saddle pony helped the team. It would have to be steady, otherwise the reins would soon be in a tangle. American horsemen make far greater use of eye snaps on tie chains, ropes and straps. British horsemen tie the appropriate knots smartly, yet must have wasted hours compared with simply snapping on to a link.

Life with the American big teams was anything but prosaic. At a recent Royal Highland Show, a Canadian visitor admiring the Clydesdales spoke of keeping several hundred horses on the family ranch in the twenties and how, after five or six times with collars on, they were considered broken. Not surprisingly, 'runaways' were a common feature. To avoid this sort of excitement, the 'tying-in and bucking-back' system was developed. A horse was tied in by passing a light coil chain from his halter to

Six-horse hitch class at the national Dairy Cattle Congress, Waterloo, Iowa. North America is as yet in advance of Britain in numbers of multiple hitches

the halter ring of the horse in the rear, and the other end to the inside trace of the horse ahead. A horse so yoked had little alternative but to follow its leader. In 'bucking back', a buck rope or strap snaps across the withers from one bit ring to the other. From behind the withers a single strap or rope runs backwards and downwards to the nearest draw or trace chain taking the strain.

In driving teams to and from the stable, the horses remain in their ranks. The lead horses are driven by means of lines to the outside pair, and the rear team is led, each being tied back to its neighbour. In the field, long feed boxes and water troughs are great time savers, enabling the whole team to be fed and watered in one operation without leaving the place of work.

A pair of good lead horses is of inestimable value to the big team driver. For this reason, a ten-horse hitch yoked two, four and four is popular. The driver need only hold the two leaders, as the rest are held back by the buck ropes. They are easier to control in the event of unruliness or even a runaway,

Clydesdale mares in working order. Ivy and Amber take part in a ploughing match wearing ear muffs in addition to other decorations

Exercising the famous forty-horse hitch owned by Richard Sparrow, Zearing, Iowa. This fascinating example of the art of yoking the big team shows how horses are coupled and tied in, and indicates the length of rein needed

and a fast lead team sets the pace for all the others. The great lead horses of the horse era were among those unsung heroes which opened up the new lands.

Two such were Toby and Bonny who led what was probably the biggest team ever assembled, and certainly in the worst conditions. A fourteen-ton waggon of wool had bogged down in a river flooded like a sea in an Australian outback. Two teams each of eighteen horses had tried to shift that load and failed, so every horse in the convoy, seventy-six, was yoked. Let Reginald Ottley tell the story:

There was a lot of bumping and boring going on. But we made it. We finally had the whole seventy-six strung out in pairs. When they were yoked, teamster 'Yacka' told Toby and Bonny to ease up; stretch the team out. It was good to see. Waggon teams are driven by voice, not reins, and the two leaned into their collars and edged forward until the whole of the team's chains were stretched out tight behind them. Every horse was standing straight, settled into his collar. Then 'Yacka' spit through his teeth and waded out twenty yards. 'Toby!', he said. 'Bonny! Wedge up there! Wedge up there, or I'll dust your hides!' Toby heaved in his collar. Bonny did the same. Behind them, one after the other, the rest of the team dipped their heads. The chains at their flanks gleamed in the water. Hoof by sucking hoof, they strained forward. 'Yacka' kept the team going. His voice urged them; coaxed them; swore at them. But you could feel his love for the horses, straining under his urging. Then, suddenly, the waggon rolled freely. It had reached hard ground, and its weight was nothing for the great team. Pounding through the water they almost bolted. But 'Yacka's' great voice held them, eased them down slowly. Prick-eared under the calling, Toby and Bonny eased their pulling. The team behind them slacked off, too, without tangling their chains . . .

Horsemanship of that order is born of necessity, but we owe it to future generations to ensure that competent horsemanship remains an accepted art, and that those skills so laboriously built up since the days of the oxen are not lost. Encouragingly, some farm colleges are once more considering the advisability of teaching youngsters the rudiments of horsemanship. A man who can plough with horses can plough with a tractor, but the converse is not true. There is more to be learnt from walking behind a team, noting the strain or ease with which they work as the soil dries or a patch of clay is reached, than is ever the case when difficulties simply entail opening the throttle an extra notch. The man who loves his horses adjusts his implements as finely as possible to ease their load, and learns much about the soil in the process. The Soil Association and the World Ploughing Organisation are both concerned about the destruction of good soil structure. In conserving our most precious asset, the soil, there is a very strong case for increasing the role of the draught horse on our fields.

10 Vehicles

Remember that the bread
you eat this day
was borne upon the
backs of horses,
in those seasons past.
Without them then
there was no harvest now,
they bore the burden
of the harvest wains,
those towering galleons of gold.

D. B. Nixon

'I have in Scotland many times seen a horse and cart conveying peats or turves, when the whole apparatus contained neither iron, leather, nor hemp. The collar or braham was made of straw, the backband of plaited rushes, and the wheels of wood only, without bush of metal, or binding of iron.' George Culley's 1794 description deals with one end of the horse vehicle spectrum, while at the other we have those massive and ornate four-wheel waggons drawn by two, and often four heavies.

There was no 'best' vehicle. Each was adapted to local circumstances and, as conditions changed, so did carts and waggons. The enormously large wheels almost the height of a man were not made by the wheelwright simply as an expression of his art; they were found by experience to cope best with the atrocious roads of their day.

The ancillary tradesmen – joiner, wheelwright, blacksmith, saddler and miller – were part and parcel of farming life. The closely-knit village communities perhaps knew little of the outside world, but they knew everything about the daily round. The joiner would note the running of his latest cart as it trundled down the village street. Its smoothness and ease on the horse would be a subject for comment in the pub, after church, at a local show or cricket match. If it lacked smoothness, the whole district would soon know. The village tradesman usually had his own bit of land. He had probably spent a year or two on a farm, had certainly helped during harvest and haytime, and knew what was needed. He had plenty of skilled labour at low rates, and apprentices as well. The existence today of carts made before World War I is testimony to the skill and materials used by village craftsmen.

A cart is a wheeled vehicle in its simplest form. It has two wheels mounted on a single axle, which takes the weight of the body. Archaeologists have shown evidence of carts in the fourth-century-BC Glastonbury lake village. The vital difference between cart and four-wheeled waggon is that the former's load must be balanced; if too far forward it presses unduly on the horse's back, if to the rear it lifts up the shafts and the horse cannot pull properly. When loading hay or corn in the field, the horseman would test the balance by lifting the shafts; if they went up easily the load was 'light on', not heavy enough in front.

Carts are smaller and cheaper than waggons. John Vince tells us that on a good road surface, a horse with a cart had to exert a pull of 51·4 lb to move a ton, compared with 68·1 lb per ton to pull a waggon. On arable land the difference was even greater. The cart horse had to exert a pull of 201 lb per ton, and a two-horse waggon needed 295·2 lb of energy for the same load. Thus a cart had 28 per cent less draft than a waggon. A ton was the standard cart load, and one horse could cope adequately with this.

Waggons appear to have been introduced to Britain from Holland in the sixteenth century when Dutchmen came to help drain the Fens, the flat lands of East Anglia being more suited to heavy vehicles than are hilly districts. In North America, waggons were more common than carts. A frame-bed dump cart was used extensively by contractors, and a rather similar cart with deeper body on plantations in the South. Another type of dump cart with body of $1\frac{1}{2}$ in hardwood tipped itself when unhooked in front. These and a coal cart are the only ones listed by Rittenhouse, against forty-eight different types of waggon. In America's pioneering days, distances and loads were large, manpower small, hence the 'new' country's predilection for four-wheelers hauled by large teams. In Britain the reverse was true.

American waggons were made for use there and then; lasting qualities were dominant in British craftsmen's minds. The hay waggon designed in Bucks County, Pennsylvania, has the curving lines in the traditional British style, but it might be more apt to compare it with the Conestoga waggon, from the valley of that name, first designed in 1755 and usually drawn by six horses. This could cross rough country and streams without being torn apart, and resembled a sea-going boat more than a factory-built waggon of later date.

Though waggon bodies differed in certain parts there is marked similarity in the undercarriage. The 4 ft 8½ in track which is standard gauge on many of the world's railways is similar to widths between waggon wheels, and tracks radiating from an ancient lake village near Meare in Somerset are marked with wooden stakes laid crosswise, each 4 ft 8 in wide! Thus is the European Bronze Age linked with a nineteenth-century waggon undercarriage.

Early waggons had little turning capacity. In some cases the design allowed no more than quarter-lock and, until means were devised of setting wheels clear of the body, or of making them small enough to turn underneath it, a very large turning circle was required. Waggons before World War I generally had no springs, and the principle of making a fore-carriage, with the front wheels turning under the body, was only adopted a few years previously.

Brakes are essential. Drug bats, skid pans, dog sticks, roller scotches and locking chains (see glossary on page 105) are among the means of slowing a cart or waggon downhill.

Communications were so poor in the nineteenth century that improved design in one district took time to filter through to the next. Culley and Bailey, writing around 1800 on *The Agriculture of Northumberland, Cumberland and Westmorland,* note the transition to one-horse carts from two-horse carts and waggons. Three single-horse carts are generally

Traditional iron-tyred farm cart fitted with wooden frame or 'gaumers' to carry bulky loads of hay or corn in sheaf or straw. The end door may be removed and the cart tipped when leading turnips or farmyard manure

The older type of wheel; front wheels have sixteen spokes, rear wheels fourteen. In heavier farm waggons, the front wheels often have fewer spokes than the rear. The wheelwright's was a specialist trade

driven by a man or a boy. One man takes three of these carts for coal every day, 26 miles there and back again, in 12 hours, carrying 72 bushels. The two-horse carts bring 36 bushels of the same coals. Thus three horses and one man, with single-horse carts, do as much work as four horses and two men with two-horse carts. The average speed quoted is over four miles per hour allowing no time for rests, meals or unloading.

Waggons were made in different forms and dimensions in different parts of Britain. According

A beautifully built bow waggon, with side timbers curving elegantly over the rear wheels. Racks or ladders in front and behind are for hay or sheaves of corn

to Marshall (1745–1819) the Gloucestershire waggon was the best in England. The body or frame was kept low by means of a crooked side-rail bending archwise over the hind wheels. The body was wide in proportion to its shallowness, and the wheels ran six inches wider than those of most other waggons. The shorter three-quarter bed had a better lock than the full bed, and could turn in 'almost as narrow a compass as a chaise', according to Rudge. For carting hay and straw, light ladders were fixed before and behind, and 'rathes' along the sides.

A double-shafted waggon. Horse decorations include fly head terrets between the ears, and breast plates with brasses attached

The Berkshire waggon was light and low-slung, but in its original form rather unmanoeuvrable. Almost as much hay or straw could be carried on the Norfolk cart and waggon, formed by adding a pair of fore wheels and shafts to a common cart, with a pole connecting axle to axle. Rood's patent waggon was a contrivance whereby the driver could change a waggon into two separate tip-carts, in a few minutes. Draft springs were invented by Sir Alex Gordon, to obviate the tugs and jolts on the teams when pulling in the ordinary way. The force of the spring was added to the force exerted by the horse, but these carriages never came into general use. Light one-horse waggons were recommended for smooth, level roads.

The great agricultural societies played a large part in the spread of better cart design. Ball's Farm Cart was exhibited at the Royal Show, Bedford, in 1874, and is in many ways similar to those we see a century later. It had removable hay ladders, its balance was good and its tipping device simple and safe. The wheels were strong and conveniently dished to give easy running and a square bearing on the road. One great advantage open to the waggon builders of that era was the supply of seasoned timber, and this is one factor that has preserved those splendid vehicles of another era. Balls also patented a low-slung two-wheel cattle cart or bull float, using the bent axle principle.

In North America, springless waggons were known as dead-axle drays, and could carry immense loads. The Owensboro was long and heavy, being used to carry rolls of newsprint to the presses, and theatrical scenery. It had heavy hubs and a

A double-shaft waggon in York. Samuel Smith's, Yorkshire's oldest brewery, have recently returned to horse power, and believe that this dray is the only one of its kind used to deliver beer in Britain

horizontal fifth wheel in front for turning. A lighter type by the same firm was fitted with shafts rather than pole, had a higher body, and low slatted sides. Its dimensions were 10 ft 6 in by 4 ft, with sides 12–20 in high, wheels 34–38 in, for either one or two horses. A four-ton dead-axle dray had a body 14 ft long by 50 in wide, 30 in sides and wheels of 34 and 38 in. A capable driver was needed to deal with such a weight.

There were over ten million horses on US farms in 1947, eight million less than in 1890, while in 1920 the total had reached twenty-six million horses. It is not surprising then that the Studebaker Company produced one waggon every five minutes. In 1948 a used cart cost $125.00.

Major improvements in cart and waggon building came too late for the horse era. Pneumatic tyres and ball bearings so reduced draft that bigger loads could be pulled, the difference being easily assessed by anyone who has had to move first an empty iron-rimmed cart and then a rubber wheeled one by himself, without the horse's aid!

Despite this, modern machine-made parts cannot compare for craftsmanship with wooden wheels, in some of which every spoke was set in a different position from rim and hub to prevent breakage when the waggon swayed from side to side. Excess weight was cut away by chamfering, each elegant curve had practical value. The bright paint was a matter of local custom, certain colours being deemed unlucky in certain areas. When factory-made waggons took over, they were still built to last, the boat shape with side-boards sloping outwards like a ship's hull being most popular.

Two more Belgians in a type of
vehicle often used for display in
North America. Box seat, back rest
and foot board make for safer
driving than on some more sparsely
furnished transports

Mr Ted Dunning, York, bought this
block rulley for half a crown
(12½p) in 1964. Renovated by a
village craftsman, it is worth well
over £100 today

11 Decorations

I have, in Berkshire and that neighbourhood, several times met a narrow-wheeled waggon, with six stallions, one before another; the first horse, besides having on a huge bridle, covered with fringe and tassels, enough to half-load a common Yorkshire cart-horse, has six bells hung to it, the next five, and so on to the last, which has only one; and it is really diverting to see with what a conceited air the driver struts and brandishes his long whip.

Culley, *Observations on Live Stock* (1794)

Horse decorations may be conveniently grouped into three main classes: those enhancing the animal itself; adornments to necessary harness; and non-essential harness embellishments such as horse brasses.

Plaiting of mane and tail is the chief method of beautifying a horse out of harness. A skilful artist brings out the arch in the animal's neck by thickening the plait to hide any natural lack of fullness. Raffia and ribbon may be braided into the mane. Small flags in line along the mane make its crest look bigger still, and different colours are chosen to contrast with body colour. Red, blue, green and yellow are the most popular.

Though there is no practical advantage in mane plaiting, tail braiding helps neatness and cleanliness. In these days of undocked tails there is a difference compared with the very short stumps previously allowed.

Bobs were originally intended to make their wearer's hindquarters more prominent, but to continue their use on an undocked tail, leaving the shorn stump dangling, is conservatism at its most senseless. A jug handle or tail loop was often formed by using a piece of wire as base for hair, ribbon and raffia. The different types of tail braiding for different breeds and in different areas make quite a study on their own.

An eye-catching elaboration of harness is the Scottish Peaked Collar, or brecham. These 'long tops' have naturally become associated with Clydesdale teams at ploughing matches, and add to the imposing stature of Scotland's heavy horse. They add to the weight the horse must carry round its neck before it can translate any energy into pulling power. South of the Border peaked collars are less common.

The housen originally performed a purely useful function, acting as a cape and preventing water trickling down between collar and shoulders. It is now solely decorative, an extra area on top of the hames to which still more fancy work may be added, but has been retained for working purposes in some parts.

98

How to plait a tail. Not every horse stands so quietly. One small boy worked by lying along the horse's back and reaching down until he could work from ground level

A well-decorated pair. Ear
muffs laid back do not disguise the
grey's distrust of the spectator.
Brasses suspended from the sides of
the collar are an unusual feature

Rosettes are an old and simple form of harness decoration. They are easily fixed at junctions, such as those of head-strap and brow-band, and the right angles of the breechings.

Fancy stitching, tassels and fringes are found on some heavy horse harness today, but the main type of decoration is the horse brass. Buckles that shine play their part, and elaborately-shaped buckles combine utility with display. Circular, oval, octagonal and other shapes of brass were originally fitted direct to the harness. There was ample scope, and the only tool needed was a sharp pricker to take the fine wire pins holding brass to leather.

Hanging pieces seem to have begun on the horse's forehead. Trade catalogues of a century ago are a guide, and those from 1870 to 1920 indicate the extent to which horsemen of the period were addicted to brasses. They also prove that complete identification with his work which was such a factor in the very high standard of horsemanship.

Brasses were made in an incredible number of patterns. Crescent, circle and star were very popular, but many brasses depicted trade motifs and heraldry. Phoenix, swan, cockerel and eagle vied with horse and lion in tradesmen's catalogues. When horses predominated in urban as well as rural transport, various trades identified themselves by using appropriate brasses. A sack, a wheatsheaf or a windmill were obvious buys for millers' teams. Brewers could have their name across a barrel, timbermen had a choice of trees, crossed saws or acorns. The farm horseman found a carter with whip in his own image, or a horse's head.

Farmers could choose from a range of stock, the cow being an exception; in the horse brass era the cow accounted for little, and in the late 1800s a dairy farmer did not ride to town in the same railway carriage as the corn and sheep men. Farmers occasionally had private brasses with their own names, but we must bear in mind that most farm brasses belonged to the men employed there, and not to the farmer.

Horses of enormous stature moved railway waggons in shunting yards, and were decorated

Horse brasses remain among the most popular ornaments in and out of stable

101

with a wide choice of design of early locomotives. Similarly, at the docks, anchor and sailing ship designs were available in range and quality that the modern collector covets. Several of the many nineteenth-century railway companies produced their own designs incorporating their monograms. Walsall, Staffordshire, now a Mecca for collectors of brasses, where many were made, was but one town with its own brasses, as London, Liverpool, Leeds and Birmingham acted similarly, and all were great employers of horse labour. Saddlers sometimes had their own brasses as advertisements, but this was a regional idea, seldom found in the north or east.

An interesting spate of brasses followed Queen Victoria's Jubilee in 1887. Commemorative brasses were struck specially for the event, a fashion which continued until World War I, and Terry Keegan in *The Heavy Horse* states that over fifty commemorative designs of Victoria were produced.

Patriotic horse ornaments introduced to celebrate the relief of Ladysmith and Mafeking had enormous sales. Both King Edward VII and King George V were portrayed on brasses, as were public figures like Disraeli and Gladstone, Lloyd George and Kitchener. The heads of Churchill and Montgomery were models after World War II when few new brasses were being used for their prime function.

Another class of brass was the award badge. Ploughing match winners found such an apt prize of lasting value, and the RSPCA awarded merit badges at the London Cart Horse parade of 1886. The Society's object was greater care in the general standards of work horse care, and other boroughs and urban councils followed suit.

The first cast brasses were dated about 1825. Before then, patterns were made by hand from hammered brass sheets of which very few remain. Cast brasses could be produced much more cheaply, and standard designs of frames were used to contain a great variety of designs. A diamond-shaped registration mark provided some protection against copying of designs by rivals from 1842 to 1883, and

this mark is sometimes found on the backs of brasses.

Around the latter date, stamping as opposed to casting of brasses began. This operation called for high capital investment, and was the first to suffer when decline in demand came after 1914. The stamped brass differs from the cast model in having a shiny surface both back and front, whereas the rougher texture of the cast brass may be seen on the back. Some stamped brasses were made one at a time, and because of small differences are sometimes confused with earlier, handmade brasses.

In the north of England, hame plates were made to decorate a strap joining the hame tops. A number of brass decorations were attached, and in the south-west a still bigger strap was used, often with a hame plate brass and other brass pieces. The saddler chose this place to put his name, as did companies sporting their own brasses.

The hame plates were often designed to match the fly terrets. These were yet another type of decoration, screwing into a fitting on the head strap or fixed to the top of the collar. The original idea seems to have been to ward off flies, but where more than one horse was working they tended to damage the terrets by constantly rubbing up and down, and perhaps catching in each other's harness. Fly terrets frequently matched the face pieces or hanging pieces, and were almost as numerous as the brasses themselves. The double fly terret had a double miniature brass which pivoted on a centre pin, and was known as a burler or tumbler in Scotland.

Yet another type of horse decoration is the floral display, which allied to wool decoration is found chiefly in Scotland. Sprays of flowers form bridges over the saddle, a crown above the britchen or the wee crown set over the typical Scotch peaked collar. Mane, hame, britchen buckle and tail decorations are added, and the fine nature of the work contrasts with the qualities usually associated with a ploughman's hands. Like the walking stick dresser, the modern horse decorator uses modern materials when these do the job better, so plastic flowers adorn leather harness and last longer than garden

Floral saddle decoration. Artificial flowers are the modern ploughman's aid, lasting longer and withstanding wet weather better. Floral decorations are a Scottish speciality

flowers. The woollen type is more traditional, but also more easily spoilt by the weather. The artists say that to make either is a better way of spending winter evenings than watching television.

How fervently lovers of the heavy horse will agree! Let us leave the last appropriate word to Richard Jefferies:

A creaking and metallic rattle, as of chains, comes across the arable field – a steady gaze reveals the dim outline of a team of horses slowly dragging the plough, their shapes indistinctly seen against the hedge. A bent figure follows, and by-and-by another distinct creak and rattle, and yet a third in another direction, show that there are more teams at work, plodding to and fro. The teams at plough are growing momentarily distinct . . .

. . . The mist vanishes – disappearing rather than floating away; a circle of blue sky opens overhead, and finally, travelling slowly, comes the sunshine over the furrows.

Tail piece! This shows the 'stretcher' to which trace chains are attached. Its purpose is to prevent traces chafing the horse's flanks. This Suffolk has a particularly neat tail braid

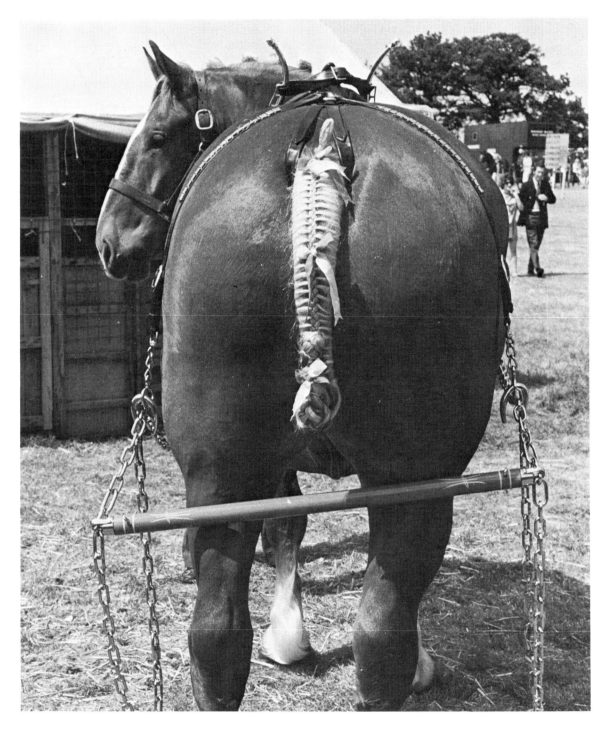

Glossary

The Horse

Mare Adult female. Brood mare is one used for breeding.

Stallion Adult uncastrated male. Also called an entire, or entire horse. In certain contexts, 'horse' may mean stallion, especially in older works.

Gelding Castrated male, more docile for working than a stallion.

Foal A young horse of either sex until one year old. It then becomes a yearling, a two-year-old, a three-year-old. Male foals are known as colt foals, females as filly foals.

Greasy leg Associated with excessive feather, and with over-feeding especially when the horse has rested in stable for a few days.

Feather Long hair round the fetlocks. A 'clean-legged' horse has little or no feather.

Strip, stripe, blaze White marking down front of face.

In the Stable

Halter Bitless headpiece of light hemp. Used when catching the horse, tying in stable. Often worn under bridle, and then used for tying up. A horseman's trick is to remove it without taking off the bridle, done through the horse's mouth.

Block, clog, manger ball, manger log, sinker, toggle, nagger, nog, plug, helter cob When tying up in stable, the halter rope or shank runs through a ring in the manger, through a hole in a piece of wood, then tied in a simple knot to prevent withdrawal.

Yoking

Yoking Attaching a horse to conveyance or implement.

Point of draft The point from where a horse pulls to maximum advantage. It is sited just in front of the shoulders and in line with its own centre of gravity and that of the object being pulled. The modern neck collar is designed to enable the horse to pull at its point of draft.

Collar Provides the point of application of the horse's power. Most collars fit round the neck, but breast collars fit across the front of the chest.

Hames of wood or iron, are fitted round the neck collar. They have hame hooks attached, to which the trace or shaft chains are fitted.

Saddle Takes the weight of the shafts, via a chain called a back band, back chain, ridge chain, with various local terms also used.

Breechings are attached to the saddle and perform a complementary function to the collar; they enable a horse to lean backwards into the load, slow it down, stop, or reverse it. (Alternative, britching)

Bridle, Blinders The headpiece to which reins are attached.

Blinkers Solid leather flaps which prevent the horse from seeing behind and sideways. An open bridle has no blinkers.

Swingletree, whippletree Wood or metal bar to take the trace chains. A set of levers arranged to cause the united strength of the horses to be exerted at one point.

Cobbletree, baulk, evener, maisletree Wood or metal bar joining swingletrees to implement in multiple yokes.

Strings Horseman's term for reins of light rope, coiled and hung on the hames when not in use.

Plough, harness, gears General terms for the horses' ploughing equipment.

Spreader General term for wooden bar used to space the trace chains apart and prevent rubbing horses' flanks. Other names: spread bat, stretch stick, stretcher, theat bar, stent.

Meeter, metre, meter straps Attach collar and hames to cart saddle.

POINTS OF THE HORSE

1 poll
2 cheek
3 crest
4 mane
5 withers
6 back
7 loins
8 croup or quarter
9 dock
10 hip joint
11 point of buttock
12 buttock
13 hamstring
14 point of hock
15 hock joint
16 feather
17 hind cannon
18 gaskin
19 stifle joint
20 flank
21 hind quarters
22 ribs (barrel)
23 point of elbow
24 chestnut
25 fore cannon
26 back tendons
27 coronet
28 pastern and pastern joint
29 fetlock joint
30 knee
31 forearm
32 breast or chest
33 point of shoulder
34 angle of lower jaw
35 windpipe
36 groove of chin
37 chin
38 jowl
39 bridge of nose
40 forehead
41 neck
42 shoulder

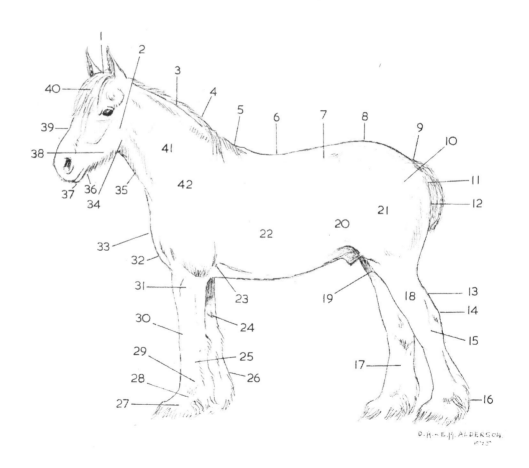

Vehicles

Sideboards Single pieces of wood to add to the capacity of the cart for solid loads such as turnips, potatoes or manure. Front board and back board are similarly used.

End door Removable wooden fitment, not hinged, at the back of the cart, lifted off to allow unloading or tipping.

Shelvings Flat wooden framework around the cart to give greater capacity for bulky loads, hay, corn in sheaf, straw. Sideboards are removed when shelvings are fitted.

Racks, Gaumers, Ladders Wooden framework set almost perpendicular from front and rear of cart or waggon, to prevent load of bulky material falling endways. Very useful, though scorned by skilled workmen.

Drug bat, shoe Types of brake used on cart or waggon.

Decoration

Horse Brasses General term for all brass decorations, whether fixed to the leather harness or suspended from it.

Martingale, breastplate, breastgirth, breast strap, chest piece Decorated strap between collar and girth.

Face piece, face brass, facer, fore plate, fore brass Broad strap hanging from brow band of bridle, and carrying a brass decoration. Often removable.

Fly head terret Brass ornament fitted to top of head strap or collar.

Kidney strap, neck strap Strap from collar to draft chains, solely for carrying decorations.

Flags, noppins, sprigs, standards, tossles Decorations standing above the plaited mane, fashioned out of straw, wire or ribbon.

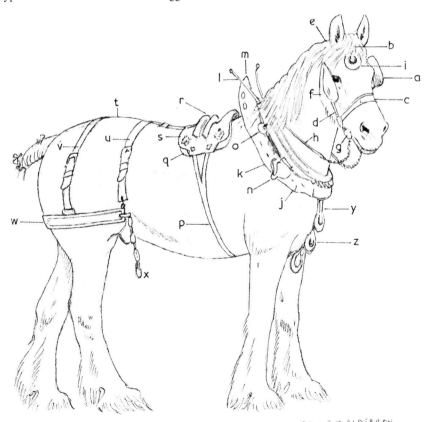

BRIDLE
a blinker
b brow band
c nose band
d cheek strap
e head strap
f throat-lash
g bit
h bearing rein, hame rein
i face piece

COLLAR
j side-piece
k body (padding)
l hames
m peak
n hame hook (for chains)
o hame ring (for reins)

SADDLE
p girth strap
q pad
r bridge
s saddle housing

BREECHINGS
t crupper
u loin strap
v hip strap
w breech band
x breechings chain

DECORATIONS
y breastplate
z brass

Appendix

Where to See Heavy Horses

March

Shire Horse Show, Peterborough
Premium Suffolk Stallion Show, Woodbridge Horse
  Show, Suffolk

May

Shropshire and West Midlands, Shrewsbury,
  Shropshire
Royal Windsor Horse Show, Home Park, Windsor
British Percheron Horse Show, Cottenham, Cambridge
Herts County Show, St Albans, Herts.
Bexhill Horse Show, Bexhill, Sussex
Suffolk Show, Ipswich, Suffolk

Spring Workings, Hasholme Carr Farm, Holme-upon-
  Spalding Moor, York
Midlands Shire Foal Sale, Derby

June

South of England Show, Ardingly, Sussex
Essex Show, Chelmsford, Essex
Bishops Waltham Show, Bishops Waltham, Hants.
Royal Norfolk, Norwich, Norfolk
Hillingdon Show, Hillingdon, Uxbridge, Middlesex
Royal Show, Stoneleigh, Warwickshire
Royal Highland Show, Ingleston, Midlothian

July

Royal Show, Stoneleigh, Warwickshire

July (continued)

Chichester Festival, Chichester, Sussex
Great Yorkshire Show, Harrogate, Yorkshire
Kent County Show, Detling, Kent
Snaith Show, Gowdall, Snaith, Yorkshire
East of England Show, Peterborough
Fordingbridge Show, Fordingbridge, Hants.

Framlingham Show, Framlingham, Suffolk
Cranleigh Show, Cranleigh, Surrey
Lambeth Show, Brockwell Park, South London
New Forest Show, Brockenhurst, Hants.
Oswestry and District, Mile House, Oswestry,
   Shropshire

August

Southsea Show, Southsea, Hants.
Hull Show, East Park, Hull, Yorkshire
Dumfries and Lockerbie, Dumfries
Essex Trade Driving Show, Brentwood, Essex
Bakewell Show, Bakewell, Derbyshire
Welwyn Hatfield Venetian Festival,

Kinross Show, Kinross House, Loch Leven
New Milton Show, New Milton, Hants.
Goosnargh and Longridge Show, Goosnargh, Preston,
   Lancashire
Mid-Somerset, Shepton Mallet, Somerset
Harlow Town Show, Harlow, Essex
Greater London Horse Show, Clapham Common,
   London SW
Billingshurst Horse Show, Billingshurst, Sussex
Alton Show, Alton, Hants.
Edenbridge and Oxted, Edenbridge, Surrey
Moorgreen Show, Watnall, Nottingham
Gillingham and Shaftesbury, Gillingham, Dorset
Melplash Show, Bridport, Dorset
Egham Show, Runnymede, Surrey
Bilsdale, North Yorkshire

September

'Yesterday's Farming' Event, Compton Pauncefoot,
   Yeovil, Somerset

High Wycombe Show, The Rye, Buckinghamshire
Alresford Show, Alresford, Hants.
Woodlarks Ploughing Match, Farnham, Surrey
Chertsey Show and Ploughing Match, Chertsey, Surrey
Romsey Show, Romsey, Hants.
West Grinstead Ploughing Match, West Grinstead,
   Sussex
East Grinstead Ploughing Match, East Grinstead,
   Sussex
Newbury Show, Newbury, Berkshire
West End Ploughing Match, West End, Surrey
Cranleigh Ploughing Match, Cranleigh, Surrey
Stokesley, North Yorkshire
Autumn Workings, Hasholme Carr Farm, Holme-
   upon-Spalding Moor, York

October

Horse of the Year Show, Wembley
Brailsford Ploughing Match, Brailsford, Derbyshire
Fairford, Fairford, Glos.
Hurstpierpoint Ploughing Match, Hurstpierpoint,
   Sussex
Surrey County Ploughing Match,

SCHHA All England Horse Ploughing Match,
   Tongham, Farnham, Surrey
East Kent Ploughing Match,

National Ploughing Match, movable fixture
Wigton Horse Sales, Cumbria

November

NE Hants. Ploughing Match,

Hampshire County Match,

Cottenham Ploughing Match, Cottenham, Cambridge

All Year Round

Courage Shire Centre, Maidenhead, Berks.: All
   aspects of management; rides on brewers' dray;
   harness display work; farriery
Percherons, Vaux Breweries Ltd, Sunderland

Bibliography

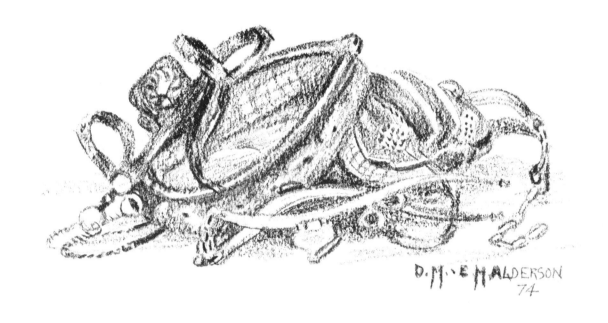

Bailey, J. and Culley, G. *Agriculture of Northumberland, Cumberland and Westmorland*, Frank Graham facsimile (1805, Newcastle-upon-Tyne)

Bell, Adrian. *Corduroy*, Hutchinson Publishing Group Ltd. (Re-issue 1974)

Culley, George. *Observations on Live Stock*, G. G. and J. Robinson (1794)

Culley, G. and Bailey, J. *Agriculture of Northumberland, Cumberland and Westmorland*, Frank Graham facsimile (1805, Newcastle-upon-Tyne)

Dickson, R. U. *Livestock*, Thomas Kelly, 17 Paternoster Row (c 1850)

Evans, George Ewart. *The Horse in the Furrow* (1960)

Gilbey, Sir Walter. *The Great Horse* (1899)

Gordon. *The Horse-World of London* (1893, reprinted Newton Abbot, 1971)

Hagedoorn, A. L. *Animal Breeding* (1939)

Horses – Mules – Power – Profit (Horse and Mule Association of America, Chicago, Illinois, 1928)

Jefferies, Richard. *The Dewy Morn* (1884). *Hodge and his Masters*

Keegan, Terry. *The Heavy Horse, Its Harness and Harness Decoration* (1973)

Lawrence, R. *Farrier*, Thomas Kelly, 17 Paternoster Row (c 1850)

The Listener. Broadcasting House, London W1A 1AA. Reginald Ottley, The Old Coach House, Kenley, Surrey

Loudon. *Loudon's Encyclopaedia of Agriculture* (1883)

Ottley, Reginald. The Old Coach House, Kenley, Surrey. *The Listener*, Broadcasting House, London W1A 1AA

Pawson, H. Cecil. *Robert Bakewell, Pioneer Livestock Breeder* (1957)

Portsmouth, Earl of. *British Farm Stock* (1950)

Prince-Sheldon, Prof. J. (Ed.). *Livestock in Health and Disease* (1901)

Rittenhouse, Jack D. *American Horse-drawn Vehicles* (Los Angeles, 1948)

Scott Watson and Hobbs. *Great Farmers* (1951)

Transactions of the Highland and Agricultural Society of Scotland, Blackwood, Edinburgh. Annual publication including photographs and details of Clydesdale Show winners, grants to horse associations, notes on heavy horse breeding and economy

Tylden, G. *Discovering Harness and Saddlery* (1971)

Trow-Smith, R. *History of British Livestock Husbandry* (1957)

Vince, John. *Discovering Carts and Wagons* (1970)

Wentworth, Lady. *The World's Best Horse* (1958)

Wright, Rev Philip. *Salute the Carthorse*

Wright, Prof Sir Robert P. (Ed.). *Standard Cyclopedia of Modern Agriculture and Rural Economy* (1908)

Youatt, William. *The Horse* (1885)

Acknowledgements

My grateful thanks are due to everyone who has assisted in the preparation of this book. In particular, thanks must go to the breed society secretaries: Roy Bird of the Shire Horse Society, East of England Showground, Peterborough; F. W. Eustis of the Ohio Belgian Breeders Association; Stuart Gilmour of the Clydesdale Horse Society of Great Britain and Ireland, 24 Beresford Terrace, Ayr, Scotland; Bruce A. Roy, of the Canadian Percheron Association, Cremona, Alberta, Canada; A. E. Vyse of the British Percheron Horse Society, Owen Webb House, Gresham Road, Cambridge and W. J. Woods of the Suffolk Horse Society, Woodbridge, Suffolk. Thanks are also due to *The Draft Horse Journal*, Waverly, Iowa; *Draught Horse* (Editor, Lee Weatherly), East Grinstead, Sussex; *The Field* and *Thelwell*.

I wish to thank the publishers and authors concerned for permission to print extracts from the following: *Corduroy* by Adrian Bell (Hutchinson Publishing Group Ltd); *Great Farmers* by James A. Scott Watson and May Elliott Hobbs (Faber and Faber Ltd); *American Horse-Drawn Vehicles* by J. D. Rittenhouse (reproduced by courtesy of Clymer Publications, Los Angeles).

The Misses Alderson are responsible for the superb line drawings. For the photographs thanks must go to: The British Museum; R. J. & C. J. Clark, Stoke by Nayland, Essex; Harold Cline, Marshalltown, Iowa, USA; Bob Lomas, Horsham, Sussex; Colin Simister, Darlington, Co Durham; Jerry Springer, Heber, Utah, USA and Kendal Webb, Park City, Utah, USA.

Finally, thanks to Richard Mitchell and to Penny Whaley who typed the manuscript.